National Association of Biology Teachers

MIDDLE SCHOOL IDEA BOOK

A compendium of previously published NABT ideas and activities adapted and reprinted for Middle School teachers and their students (grades 5-8)

Edited by Catherine A. Wilcoxson, Ph.D.
Department of Biological Sciences
Northern Arizona University
Flagstaff, Arizona

Published by the National Association of Biology Teachers (NABT)
11250 Roger Bacon Drive, #19, Reston, Virginia 20190-5202

ISBN 0-941212-22-X

Printed in the United States of America by Automated Graphic Systems, White Plains, Maryland.

The wonderful drawings that appear on the cover, chapter heading pages, and on page 67 are courtesy of Chris John Cluster. NABT sincerely appreciates his creative efforts on its behalf.

About This Book

Middle school students are unique individuals. Their interests and abilities are expanding, and their capacities to engage in detailed, hands-on activities and discussions of a wide range of scientific topics are beginning to bloom. For this reason, the middle school years (grades 5-8) should not be regarded as a sort of "way station" between the lower elementary grades and high school but rather viewed as an opportunity to challenge middle schoolers to begin to develop the methods and skills that will help them seek answers to questions throughout their lives. By capturing their enthusiasm and piquing their curiosity, teachers can begin here to provide the foundation that will inspire these students to become creative problem solvers and encourage them to consider pursuing scientific careers.

NABT is pleased to provide for all middle school educators a new monograph that deals specifically with teaching middle level students. This manual offers teachers a variety of proven activities that were selected and edited to reflect middle level philosophy, the National Science Education Standards (1996), and Benchmarks for Scientific Literacy (1993).

The **Middle School Idea Book** is divided into five chapters, each with a different focus. Each section contains hands-on activities that provide many exciting and fun experiences for adolescents. In every chapter, exercises are included that will help students learn new concepts and apply them to solve real-world problems. Issues are introduced that encourage students to wonder, to ask questions, and to develop knowledge and skills through classroom interactions.

Biology is presented as an active process in these activities. Students are observing, describing, asking questions and pursuing answers to those questions, inferring, formulating conclusions, and communicating results. The monograph reflects the belief that, "Learning science is something students do, not something that is done to them" (National Research Council, 1996, p. 2).

Current topics were used to generate a series of interrelated activities that focus on the interests and concerns of young adolescents. This approach accomplishes two goals. First, it gives the students the opportunity to study in depth and in an interdisciplinary fashion a topic that interests them. According to many educators, such an approach is needed in order for students to develop understandings. We know that, "Learning important ideas in any useful way simply takes more time than has usually been assumed, at least in part because many ideas in science and mathematics are abstract and not in accord with everyday experience" (AAAS, 1993, p. 321). Second, "If we want genuine learning, we must begin with the questions and concerns of young adolescents and help them to find answers and meanings that they may integrate into their understanding of themselves and their world" (Beane, 1192, p. 36).

Student reflection is included to aid the sense-making process. For this reason, journal writing, class presentations, and student projects are included in many of the activities in this publication. Students communicate their results, what they have learned, their problem-solving process, and the questions they still have about the topic. The use of cooperative groups and the communication of results and problem-solving strategies facilitate learning.

The **Middle School Idea Book** is a resource that offers a variety of activities for teachers to choose from — or they may decide to implement them all. Whatever the choice, we are all challenged to involve our students in learning about our world. Too often, we forget that, "Young adolescents are real people living real lives in a real world" (Beane, 1992, p. 35).

Moreover, although this publication was developed with middle school life science teachers in mind, educators at the high school and elementary levels may also find a gem or two here that they can use in their classes, depending upon the student populations they serve. Since the skills we focus on here are used in science classes at all levels, it is possible that with some modification — and a healthy dose of teacher ingenuity — most of these ideas and exercises could be used by students of all ages.

References

American Association for the Advancement of Science. (1993). Benchmarks for Scientific Literacy, New York: Oxford University Press.

Beane, J.A. (1992). Turning the floor over: Reflections on a middle school curriculum. Middle School Journal, January, 34-40.

National Science Education Standards (1996). Washington, DC: National Academy Press.

Acknowledgments

My sincere appreciation to Dr. Wayne Carley, Executive Director, National Association of Biology Teachers, for granting permission to adapt and reprint the following activities originally found in NABT publications. Many thanks go to the entire NABT staff for their help and support during the publishing process — especially to Sherry Grimm, Michele Bedsaul, and Christine Chantry, whose editorial expertise is much appreciated.

I am very grateful to the following authors of the original activities selected for this book. Although some liberties were taken in expanding and modifying their exercises to conform to today's recommended middle school methods and philosophy, I trust that the spirit of the activities has remained intact.

Sharon J. Fisher
North High School
Des Moines, IA

Stanley L. Weinberg
156 E. Alta Vista Avenue
Ottumwa, IA

Catherine Wilcoxson
Northern Arizona University
Flagstaff, AZ

Nancy Chartier Balcolm
University of Connecticut
Cooperative Extension Service
Hamden, CT

David A. Wright
Northeast Magnet School of Science,
Engineering & the Visual Arts
Wichita, KS

Emmett L. Wright
Kansas State University
Manhattan, KS

Karen Travers
Delaware Nature Society
Hockessin, DE

Barbara Cauchon
Brookline High School
Brookline, MA

Kevin Collins
Sandpoint Middle School
Sandpoint, ID

Susan K. Johnson
Monona Grove High School
Madison, WI

Mary R. Chappell
Kellam High School
Virginia Beach, VA

William F. McComas
University of Southern California
Los Angeles, CA

Duane H. Keown
University of Wyoming
Laramie, WY

Kathryn V. Lykins
Shorter College
Rome, GA

Douglas J. Glasenapp
Rufus King High School
for the College Bound
Milwaukee, WI

Judith L. Allard
Burlington High School
Burlington, VT

Finally, a special thank you goes to the following professors, teachers, and students who reviewed and researched the activities included in this manual. The research into teaching and learning provided valuable insights, but it is because of the personal knowledge and expertise of the reviewers that it was possible to develop this monograph into what will hopefully be a truly valuable resource for all teachers.

NABT Publications Committee
Monograph Subcommittee

Richard D. Storey, Chair
The Colorado College
Colorado Springs, CO

Michael P. Clough
Memorial High School
Eau Claire, WI

Maura Flannery
St. John's University
Jamaica, NY

Katrina Kim Leeman
Southside Junior High School
Manchester, NH

David Masterman
Seattle, WA

Betsy Ott
Tyler Junior College
Tyler, TX

Dan Wivagg
Baylor University
Waco, TX

Reviewers and Content Specialists

Gordon Johnson
Northern Arizona University
Flagstaff, AZ

Bob Swift
Northern Arizona University
Flagstaff, AZ

Jack States
Northern Arizona University
Flagstaff, AZ

Dick Shand
Northern Arizona University
Flagstaff, AZ

Gary Bateman
Northern Arizona University
Flagstaff, AZ

Steve Shuster
Northern Arizona University
Flagstaff, AZ

Tina Ayers
Northern Arizona University
Flagstaff, AZ

Marcia Bateman
Flagstaff Public Schools
Flagstaff, AZ

Karen Clayton
Fountain Hills High School
Fountain Hills, AZ

Laura Pellegrini
Highland High School
Gilbert, AZ

Susan Holiday
Leupp Middle School
Flagstaff, AZ

Jodi Crose
West Sedona School
Sedona, AZ

Deb Romanek
Nebraska Department of Education
Lincoln, NE

Lenny VerMaas
Norris High School
Norris, NE

Dot Snesrud
Osceola Elementary School
Osceola, NE

Scott Byington
Nash Community College
Rocky Mount, NC

Susan Blunck
University of Maryland
College Park, MD

Preservice and Graduate Students
Northern Arizona University

Dave Bereson
Dan Higgins
Velyda Meyeres
Liz Nelson
Michael Nordstrand
T.J. Wheeler
Cathy Corley
Robert DeGroot
Jon Devenney
Michelle Gallon
Danielle Klein
Danna Lagerquist
Jennifer Leware
Michelle Mioduski
Matt Olson
Kim Ramsey
Bob Richert
Craig Rowe
Frank Stacey
Valerie Yellen
Tammy Yonnie
Mike Valenzuela
Angela Wilson

Preservice and Graduate Students
University of Nebraska

Tom Applegate
David Crowther

Table of Contents

About This Book 3

Acknowledgments 5

Chapter 1 — Observations and Presentations 9
- Adopt a Tree Project 11
- The Snail 17
- Cooperative Controversies 21

Chapter 2 — Marine Activities in Landlocked Classes 27
- Using Marine Aquaria 29
- Songs of Giants: Bioacoustics in Cetaceans 35

Chapter 3 — Food Explorations 39
- Pizza Analogy 41
- The Fungi Feast 47
- Food for Thought 51
- The Fruit Lab 60

Chapter 4 — Evolutionary Investigations 65
- Variation and Adaptation at the Zoo 67
- Demonstrating Population Growth 75
- How Long Is a Long Time? 79

Chapter 5 — Classification Studies 91
- Teaching Classification with Music 93
- The Nuts and Bolts of Classification 97
- Life Science Scavenger Hunt 101

About the Editor 107

Chapter 1
Observations and Presentations

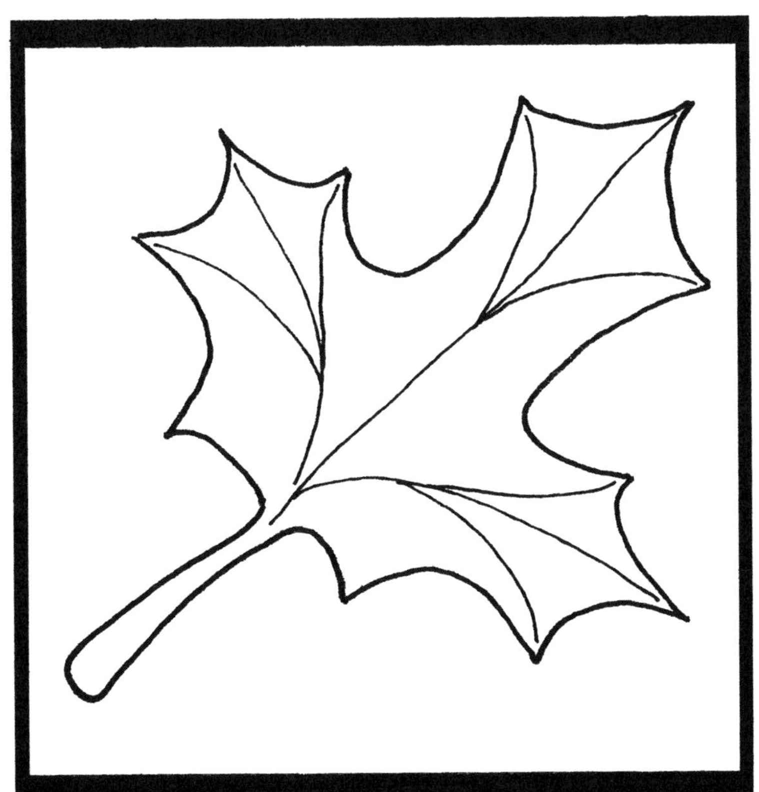

Adopt a Tree Project

Adapted from an original activity by Sharon J. Fisher

There are many different kinds of trees. Trees have existed for more than 200 million years and are the largest life form to inhabit the Earth. Like people, trees have special characteristics that help us recognize them. Too often, however, we overlook the trees in our environment. This project is an introduction for small group investigations of questions or topics relating to trees that students would like to explore.

OBJECTIVES

- Students will observe, collect, record, organize, and present biological data.

- Students will engage in a life science field experience.

- Students will investigate one tree species.

- Students will practice written and spoken communication skills.

MATERIALS

This project can be done with materials that students have around the house or that are available at school.

TEACHING TIPS

- Students need to spend more time in direct observation of nature. This project requires an extended period of time for students to complete the required investigation and is intended to familiarize students with a very common part of their environment, a tree. It cannot be just any old tree, however, but a special tree — their tree.

- A few days before beginning the unit, place current news articles about trees on a bulletin board to stimulate student interest and thinking. Articles may describe damage to trees by acid rain, destruction of rain forest /Everglades, effect of urbanization on plants, etc.

- Have the students work in cooperative groups of two to encourage student discussion of their observations and findings. However, each student should maintain his/her own journal.

- Begin the project immediately at the beginning of the school year. Although a large portion of the work is meant to be done outside of class, teachers should check several times to be sure their students do not put the report off until the last minute.

- Teachers who use this activity may want to introduce the exercise by having students observe tree branches with leaves that have contrasting leaf size, shape, color, and type, as well as contrasts in tree bark. Divide the class into groups of three or four students to discuss questions such as: What shape are the leaves? Are the leaves across from each other, spread out from a central point, or do they alternate from one side of the branch to the other? What is the name of the tree that this branch came from? Where does it grow? What color do the leaves turn in the fall? Do the leaves fall off in the winter? After answering these questions, call attention to the articles on the bulletin board.

• Ask students to tell why they think trees are important or tell about their experiences with trees. Ask if they have favorite trees in their yards at home. Follow this introductory activity with student investigation of a specific tree.

• Some help may be needed in showing students how to press and preserve collected leaves. If a laminator is not available, clear contact paper works well.

• Students will need access to the library in order to do the research portion of the project. Some time will also be required to show students how to calculate the height of their chosen trees.

• It is recommended that computers be used to organize, summarize, and display data.

• After the students have communicated their findings to the rest of the class, have the class discuss possible reasons for differences. What are some of the factors influencing tree growth? What kinds of trees grow around the school? In their town? What happens when a tree dies? What is the difference between an evergreen tree and a deciduous tree? What does a tree look like on the inside? These questions or student generated questions may be selected for small group investigations.

• Collaborate with history and math teachers to incorporate writing, especially bibliographies; history of the area and its development; and analysis of numerical data, especially graphing. An interdisciplinary approach is very helpful and beneficial for students.

PROCEDURE

1. Make copies of each of the three worksheet pages that follow this activity and be sure that each student or student group has received all three pages. In class, review the requirements for the investigation outlined on the worksheets.

2. Divide the class members into pairs and direct each student pair to choose a tree to observe in order to complete the investigation outlined in the "Adopt a Tree Project — Procedure for the Student" pages.

EXTENSIONS

• Have each pair of students measure off a square meter of earth and investigate the area. Record and describe all plants growing there, insects, evidence of other life forms (tracks, feathers, droppings, etc.), soil, rocks, the number of hours of sunshine that the plot receives daily, and any other characteristics that students consider interesting. Have the groups compare results and discuss factors influencing biodiversity. It is important to schedule some time for whole class discussions. The opportunity to compare results broadens and reinforces student understanding of ecosystems.

• Explore the effects of soil type, amount of sunlight, and climate on tree growth. Draw a map locating the tree species.

• Investigate interactions among trees (producers) and other organisms. Create a food chain.

• Campaign to improve the school surroundings by selecting and planting trees on the school grounds.

• Introduce change over time by investigating the effect of urbanization, population expansion, agriculture, industrialization, etc., on the carbon and oxygen cycle.

• Do a census of a specific tree species in a several block area near the school, extrapolate to the city, and estimate the population of a specific tree species. Explore some real world examples where this sampling method might be used to do data analysis. What might be some factors that would influence the number of tree species that could be counted in another plot? Sample shaded areas, developed areas, and heavy traffic areas to show impact on tree populations.

SUMMING UP

This is a wonderful way to get students outside to actually observe nature. This activity supports and encourages active student learning through concrete and continuous interactions with the world around them. It provides a link to many other areas of study throughout the year, and the students will always remember their trees.

ORIGINAL SOURCE

Fisher, Sharon J. (1993). Adopt a tree project. In L.R. Sanders (Ed.), *Favorite Labs from Outstanding Teachers — Volume II* (pp. 97-99). Reston, VA: National Association of Biology Teachers.

Adopt a Tree Project — Procedure for the Student

This project will take several weeks for you to complete. It consists of several parts — collection, measurement and observations, daily observations, research, and final report. Do not write on these work sheets. Answer the questions on separate sheets of paper.

COLLECTION

1. Working with a partner, choose a mature tree that can be visited easily and often. Choose a DECIDUOUS tree, not a pine tree or an evergreen. If possible, select a tree that you can readily identify by observing leaf characteristics. Books and CD-ROMs can be found in the library or classroom, if necessary, to help identify the tree.

2. Collect 5-6 leaves from the tree *before* and *after* they begin to change color in the fall. Preserve the leaves by pressing and laminating them.

3. Make a bark rubbing of the tree. Place a very thin piece of paper or cotton cloth over the bark and, using the flat, long side of a crayon, carefully rub the paper or cloth until the bark's pattern shows through. Repeat until you have a a rubbing with which you are happy. What do you think is the function of the bark? What is the effect when animals, such as rabbits and deer, eat the bark?

MEASUREMENTS AND OBSERVATIONS

Create a data table and graph information when possible. In some cases, drawings will be needed. Use colored pencils and make accurate and complete sketches.

1. Calculate the tree's height.

2. Measure the circumference or distance around the trunk. Use a crayon and ruler to mark in several places $4^1/2$ feet up from the ground. With a tape measure or string and ruler, measure the distance around the trunk at this height.

3. Estimate the age of the tree. Compare estimation strategies with at least two other groups. Interview people who live nearby and/or city park employees to determine when the tree was planted.

4. Draw the general shape of the tree. Is it shaped like an umbrella? Is it tall or slim, or is it flat, rounded or pointed on top?

5. Locate a terminal bud — that's the bud at the very end of a branch. Measure how much the branch grew during the last growing season by following the branch back from the terminal bud until the first growth rings can be seen. (These will be rings around the branch, and they show where the terminal bud was last year.)

6. Sketch the branch, including at least five (5) lateral (side) buds and the terminal bud. This will show the pattern or arrangement of leaves on the branch.

7. If the tree is bearing fruit (including nuts), sketch one. How are the seeds of the tree dispersed?

8. Examine the tree for any trauma caused by the wind, ice, lightning, fire, insects, or people. Speculate from these observations as to the condition of the tree. Is it healthy? Are there any advantages or disadvantages to the tree being located where it is? What is the natural environment of the tree? Try to remember the tree during other seasons; how is it different?

DAILY OBSERVATIONS

Each student in your group should maintain his/her own journal that includes the most important idea or new information that you learned each observation day. This journal should also include the following information:

- The first signs of leaves turning color.
- The date the first leaves began to fall.
- Reports of any animals that might be using the tree for a temporary or permanent home.
- Signs of disease or fungi on the tree.
- Descriptions of any lichen growing there.
- Descriptions of any other damage to the tree in any way.

OPTIONAL

Take the length and width measurements of 100 leaves from the tree. Calculate the mean, mode, and range of size. Graph the data.

RESEARCH

References will be needed to determine the scientific name of the tree. Scientific classification is a way of describing living things while showing their relationships to others. This part of the project will require library work.

1. Research information about the species of your tree. Where did it come from? Was it brought to this country or is it a native tree? What is this tree good for? Are there any commercial products made from the tree? Does the tree species have any historical value or is it famous for anything? Look for interesting facts and myths about the tree. Some trees are considered very magical or holy by different groups of people.

2. Is the tree a soft or hardwood tree? What is the average life span of this tree species? Find a picture of the tree's flower and fruit (yes, it will have them) and sketch them. Be sure to color your sketch.

3. Make any additional comments about this tree or about trees in general that would add to the quality of the report.

FINAL REPORT

Your final work may take any form you like as long as it includes everything required below. Notebook reports or large posters can be made, and except for the collection part, it is even possible to do the whole report on video.

EACH REPORT SHOULD INCLUDE:

1. Some kind of introduction or cover page with student name, period, date, and name of the tree. If posters are made, they still need titles.

2. Collected leaves, bark rubbing, and sketches.

3. Measurements and observations arranged in a logical order. Data tables, graphs, drawings, etc., should be used to show that you have taken the time to make sense out of the information you have gathered.

4. Journal entries.

5. Tree classification.

6. Research that tells more detail about the tree species.

7. Additional questions you may have about your tree or trees in general. What are some additional things you would like to find out about trees?

8. Bibliography. This includes all the books, magazines, videotapes, CD-roms, etc., used to obtain information.

9. *Extra* — A photograph of you, your partner, and your tree; collected leaves that are in the process of changing colors; some ideas that would help conserve and care for trees.

The Snail

Adapted from an original activity by Stanley L. Weinberg

This is an activity based on the observation of a living animal. It has proven to be of great interest to students. It is excellent for beginning the year's work, as it provides a lively introduction to laboratory work.

In addition, the exercise also provides students with opportunities to explore, to share their findings with others, and to design investigations to answer their own questions. The teacher observes with the students and asks questions that motivate students to investigate further and to link the new findings to their current level of understanding.

OBJECTIVES

- Students will observe and record snail movements and behavior and will communicate their discoveries and questions to the class in written reports and class presentations.

- Students will design and conduct a snail investigation and present their findings.

MATERIALS

- snails
- watches
- compasses
- lettuce
- glass plates
- 6" squares
- rulers
- hand lenses and stereomicroscopes
- sandpaper

TEACHING TIPS

- Several types of snails may be used for this activity. The white, edible Burgundy snail, *Helix pomatia,* is a good choice. Other edible snails, *Otala lactea* or *petit gris,* are less active and, therefore, less useful. These imported snails are sometimes available in fish markets in major cities. The common garden pest, *Helix aspersa*, is quite lively. It can be collected at night or in daytime on a rainy day. These and other snails are also available at relatively steep prices from biological supply houses.

- Other gastropods may be substituted for H*elix*, including local land and pond snails, aquarium mystery snails, slugs, and marine forms such as periwinkles or whelks. Mystery snails are available in pet shops and in pet departments of department and variety stores.

- A pound contains about 100 snails. This is enough for a class and can be used over and over again for two or three days. As the snails die, however, dispose of them quickly. Dead mollusks become odorous very rapidly.

- Purchased snails will arrive dry with the aperture of each shell closed by a mucous membrane. Place the snails in several covered jars, with a little water and a few lettuce leaves in the bottom of each. Within a half hour, many of the snails will emerge from their shells and crawl up the glass.

- If the snail withdraws into its shell, have the student return it to the jar and take another.

Temporarily inactive snails can be reactivated by rinsing them in running water.

PROCEDURE

1. Take the jars into class. Have the students gently pick up a snail and place it on a glass plate for observation. Remind the students that a snail is a living creature and can be hurt. Caution students to handle the snails gently.

2. Ask students what they know about snails. Write down all comments, whether correct or incorrect. Tell the students that they are going to work in pairs to observe and record snail movement and behavior.

3. Divide the students in the class into teams of two.

4. Pass out copies of the "Student Data Sheet" that follows this activity and be sure each team has all the materials needed to perform the activities described on the sheet.

5. Give student teams ample time to complete the activity and write a summary of their results, along with any questions they still have about snails.

6. Ask a representative of each pair of students to present their findings and questions to the class.

7. Ask students what else they might want to find out about snails and how they might go about answering their questions.

8. Divide students into groups and have them answer one of the student-generated questions or have them come up with a question or topic they would like to explore.

9. Provide opportunities for these groups to investigate and find the answers to the questions they have selected. Experiments must be approved by the teacher before students proceed.

10. Allow ample time for groups to complete their investigations. Have each group present its findings to the class.

11. Revisit the initial lists of what students said they knew about snails, asking probing questions and correcting any inaccuracies.

12. Generate a new list of information that students have learned about snails.

EXTENSIONS

- Weigh and measure the snails.

- Discuss variation in size and weight with the class.

ACKNOWLEDGMENT

This lesson was originally published in *Biology Laboratory Manual* authored by Mr. Weinberg, published by Allyn and Bacon, Inc.

ORIGINAL SOURCE

Weinberg, Stanley L. (1990). The snail. In R.V. Hairston (Ed.), *The Responsible Use of Animals in Biology Classrooms, Including Alternatives to Dissection* (pp. 84-86). Reston, VA: National Association of Biology Teachers.

The Snail — Student Data Sheet

Working in pairs, perform all of the following activities with your snail specimen. Answer the questions asked and record your findings. Use the findings in Steps 1-12 to write a report about your snail investigations. Use extra sheets of paper, if necessary.

(The following directions are prepared for use with edible land snails. They can be slightly modified if only water snails are available.)

1. Put the snail on the glass plate and watch it for a few minutes. How does it move? If the snail does not emerge from its shell and become active within three minutes, return it to the jar and take another snail that has emerged.

2. Time the rate of movement. A sheet of paper placed under the glass plate and marked with concentric circles spaced equal distances apart will be helpful. Take the average of several trials. Give the results in table form.

3. Place the snail on sandpaper and time its motion. Compare these trials with the results from Step 2. Graph results.

4. Replace the snail on the glass plate and turn the plate on edge. What does the snail do? How can you explain its action?

5. The part of the body on which the snail moves is called the *foot.* Pick the plate up and look through the glass at the underside of the foot. What do you see happening that explains the method of movement?

6. Put a small piece of lettuce directly in front of the snail. How does it eat? Use the hand lens or stereo microscope to help you see what is happening.

7. At the front of the foot are four *tentacles.* What do they do? Touch them gently with a pencil, one at a time. What do they do now?

8. Devise a means of blocking the snail from the light. Use the hand lens or stereo microscope to try to find the snail's eyes.

9. Look at your snail's shell and at some of the shells around you. Do they all curl the same way or in different ways? How do you explain your observations?

10. Poke the foot gently with a pencil until the snail draws into its shell. How does it do this? How is it now protected? (This structure is called the *operculum.*)

11. Wait very quietly for three or four minutes, and the snail may again emerge from its shell. Just how does it do this?

12. What additional questions do you have about snails? What else would you like to know about snails?

RESULTS

Give in table form your numerical results from Steps 2 and 3. Briefly record your other results and explanations.

CONCLUSIONS AND DISCUSSION

1. What activities and traits did you see in the snail that are characteristic of living things in general?

2. What characteristics of living things did you not see?

3. How is the snail markedly different from other animals with which you are familiar?

Cooperative Controversies

An original activity by Catherine A. Wilcoxson

Scientific literacy is an ambitious national education goal that needs to be specifically addressed by classroom science teachers. A scientifically literate person asks questions and is able to investigate, explain, discriminate, and offer solutions to problems related to personal and worldwide affairs. "Scientific literacy also implies the capacity to pose and evaluate arguments based on evidence and to apply conclusions for such arguments appropriately" (National Science Education Standards, p. 22).

The ability to reason, analyze information, and make responsible decisions can be fostered by engaging students in "cooperative controversies." Controversies are interesting debatable issues to be explored and resolved. Cooperative controversy (Johnson & Johnson 1988) is a method that can be readily used in middle level classrooms to motivate students to learn about a specific topic, to listen to conflicting viewpoints, and to work together to develop a consensus position based on facts. A cooperative atmosphere encourages students to think through conflicting ideas, increases learning, and improves relationships.

The thorough examination of a relevant issue provides students an opportunity to learn science in the context of real life experiences. As students investigate an issue, they not only learn the science involved but are able to relate what they learn to societal issues and their own lives. The context drives the search for relevant information and is a key factor to learning (Yager 1996).

The purpose of the following activity is to provide a means for students to think about a problem holistically, to see connections between various aspects, and to become aware of the many levels of effect that are created by community, state, national, and worldwide problems. In this activity, the focus is on teamwork and the exploration of all possible facts and explanations to arrive at a concerted plan of action.

OBJECTIVES

- Students will research a societal issue related to life science.

- Students will develop skills in understanding complex issues from different perspectives.

- Students will develop a portfolio containing researched information, team summaries, and a final paper.

- Students will practice their written and spoken communication skills.

- Students will work on developing team member skills: how to listen and ask questions.

MATERIALS

- 3"x5" or 5"x7" note cards
- student worksheet
- a collection of CD-ROMs, videodiscs, Internet, etc. — classroom or designated library time to research the chosen life science issue.
- access to computers to do a complete written report.

TEACHING TIPS

• Ask students to brainstorm societal issues that interest them and list them on the blackboard so all class members can see and think about them. After all the issues have been listed, help the students define the specific question or issue they would like to investigate. If possible, select a problem of local interest that the students may be able to impact. Keep the topic broad enough so that several aspects can be readily researched by students. This allows class members to see a complex problem holistically from several different perspectives, increases student learning, and avoids monotonous class presentations.

A good topic will have several aspects that can be explored as subtopics for cooperative controversies. For example, the *quality of water* might be selected as the broad life science topic, with several societal issues, such as agricultural runoff, acid rain, oil spills, urbanization, irrigation, thermopollution, ocean dumping, sewage treatment, logging, etc., as subtopics to investigate. Specific water quality issues of local concern, such as the effects of various water users in the community on water quality, could also be included. Topics that may conflict with the personal values of students or their parents should be avoided.

• After choosing a life science topic and societal issues to research, ask the class to identify possible resources for obtaining information.

• Randomly assign the students to heterogeneous groups (teams) of four and give each group a societal issue about the main life science topic to research. Designate two members of each group to present one viewpoint of the societal issue and ask the other two group members to represent the opposing viewpoint. This is best accomplished by random selection. For instance, one pair of group members might present the viewpoint that agricultural runoff <u>does affect</u> the quality of water, while the other two members represent the viewpoint that agricultural runoff <u>does not affect</u> water quality.

• The goal is for the two pairs of students in each group to gather, analyze, synthesize, and evaluate the information they find about their respective viewpoints — and the issue in general — and for each pair to present their findings to the other pair of group members. The team of four will compare and contrast ideas and opinions, develop a solution, write a group report, and give a class presentation.

• Time for research should be allotted, and all groups (teams) should work together in the class or in the library for several days to gather evidence to use in their arguments and presentation. A student worksheet provides some guidance and structure to the activity. Information relevant to each team's societal issue should be written on note cards (complete with bibliographical material on the source of the information). Encourage students to consult with local and state experts, such as the Department of Game and Parks. Each pair of group members should also be given some private time to organize and practice their arguments before it is their assigned time to present them to the other two members of their team.

• While the teams are assembling their research information and practicing their arguments, the teacher will visit each group and listen to its small group presentation. Each pair of students will present the arguments and evidence that support the viewpoint it has been assigned to the other members of their team. The purpose of this initial small group presentation is to clarify each pair's position with regard to the issue the group has investigated. Encourage questions here but do not allow students to argue at this time. Sharing perspectives encourages group members to pool their knowledge and to learn from one another.

• It may be necessary to call time out periodically to give the team members presenting an opportunity to prepare new arguments or gather additional data. (Depending on the time given to each presentation and the amount of class time remaining, teachers may want to move on to the next group and come back to the first group at a later time.) Encourage students to be creative when introducing evidence by using photos, drawings, graphs, dramatizations, etc.

- In addition, at any time during the small group presentations, the teacher can call for a reversal of roles. This encourages all team members to listen closely so that they can use their best arguments. A good time for reversal is near the end of the class period because it helps recap what has been said, and presenting the other viewpoint encourages group members to end on an amiable note.

- Emphasize that the goal is to find the most rational answer. Students can disagree with ideas, not individuals. Listening to all viewpoints and information is critical, as it will be necessary to compare and contrast ideas in order to write the final consensus report. Let the students know that, in addition to researching their own viewpoint, they will also be asked to take the conflicting perspective so that they can understand the opposite viewpoint. Stress that all viewpoints and ideas are to be respected.

- The group presentation of its report to the entire class gives students practice talking in front of a large group and in expressing their opinions in a rational, thoughtful manner.

- An interdisciplinary team teaching approach can be very helpful in planning this activity. The English or public speaking teacher can help in planning and organizing the oral and written presentations. The history teacher can contribute a historical perspective of the issues. The math instructor can help students understand statistics, read and prepare graphs, use numbers to compare, etc. If possible, incorporate the use of computers both in researching information and preparing the written report. Enlist the help of as many teachers as you can to broaden the involvement of students and improve the quality of the research.

PROCEDURE

1. Heterogeneously group the students in the class into groups of four members each.

2. Designate each pair of two students in the group to represent a pro or con position with regard to the societal issue that has been assigned to their group.

3. Students conduct research of their assigned major life science issue and collect evidence to support the position they have been asked to present to the opposing pair of students in their group. Students create note cards and begin the worksheet that follows this activity.

4. Each pair of group (team) members prepares a summary (3-5 minutes) of its position to present to the other two team members and the teacher. Supporting material and substantiating evidence should be included in this small group presentation. Encourage students to restate ideas presented to make sure they understand them correctly.

5. Each pair (pro and con) argues the strengths of its position, cites supporting evidence, and reveals the weaknesses of the other viewpoint. A time-out may be called by the teacher or the team to prepare new arguments.

6. At any time during the small group session, the teacher may call for a reversal, so all team members must listen closely so that they can use their best arguments.

7. After the small group presentation, all four team members drop their assigned roles and work as a foursome toward a compromise

position about their issue. The group writes a single report that includes a brief description of each position, the group consensus, and supporting explanations. Each member of the group signs the report. The signatures indicate that they agree with the report and can explain and justify it. If consensus cannot be reached, both a majority and a minority opinion report can be submitted.

8. Finally, the group gives a brief presentation to the class on its report, followed by questions and discussion.

9. After all group presentations, enlist the help of the class to summarize the various aspects of the life science topic chosen and what the students have learned about the issue. Devise an action plan to help find a solution for this issue. This may involve writing letters to appropriate people, attending town council meetings, organizing a litter cleanup, etc.

SUMMING UP

Middle school students like to be actively involved in seeking information and applying it to real-life issues that are of interest to them. Cooperative controversy is a wonderful technique for involving students in their own learning, linking society and science, and encouraging students to learn from one another. What could be a better model for future citizens who must work together to resolve problems? Through cooperative controversy, students can learn to evaluate data objectively and reach consensus about actions that need to be taken to address complex topics in the future.

REFERENCES

Johnson, R.T. & Johnson, D.W. (1988). Critical thinking through structured controversy. *Educational Leadership,* 58-64.

National science education standards, 1996. Washington, DC: National Academy Press.

Yager, R.E. (Ed.). (1996). *Science/technology/ society as reform in science education.* Albany, NY: University of New York Press.

Cooperative Controversies — Student Work Sheet

1. The issue you are researching is ______________________________

2. The main points supporting your position are:

3. Listen to the other members of your team explain their position. Jot down notes and questions.

4. As the teams discuss the issues, write down the facts that support each viewpoint. This is a complex issue, and you need to understand both viewpoints to write a good report.

5. Change chairs and reverse positions by arguing the other team pair's position. What are some new facts that you could introduce that the other pair of group members did not think to present?

6. Summarize how the two positions are alike and how they are different.

Alike	Different

7. What are the key facts supporting each position? Reach consensus on some strategies that would improve the situation.

8. Use the information recorded in Questions 1-7 to prepare a written report signed by all group members. Be prepared to present your report to the class.

Chapter 2

Marine Activities in Landlocked Classes

Using Marine Aquaria

Adapted from original activities by Nancy Chartier Balcolm, David A. Wright, and Emmett L. Wright

A marine aquarium in the classroom brings a bit of the living ocean to students and provides a potential focus for the middle schooler's boundless fascination and interest in the sea. Using modern techniques, the establishment and maintenance of a marine aquarium can be successfully accomplished.

A marine aquarium is more expensive to set up but well worth the expense. This exercise offers suggestions for using marine aquaria as an instructional tool. Books on setting up an aquarium are listed in the references, and additional help can be found by contacting your local pet store.

OBJECTIVES

- Students will establish a balanced living system in a marine aquarium.

- Students will conduct a series of observations followed by small group investigations.

- Students will maintain an observation journal focusing on water chemistry, specific organisms, and interactions among organisms.

MATERIALS

To set up a marine aquarium, you will need the following items:

- glass tank that holds at least 30 gallons of water. (The tank should be low and wide, rather than high and deep, be well supported, and be set away from sunlight, drafts, and heat sources.)
- subgravel filter system (filter plate with lift tubes)
- filter media
- filter canister or wet/dry filter
- water conditioner
- air pump (at least 185 gallons/hour)
- natural substrate (crushed coral, oyster shells, and live sand)
- heater (calibrated to tank size)
- artificial sea water (sea salt or ocean crystals and water)
- nitrifying bacteria or live rock
- hood with fluorescent light with blue spectrum to reduce evaporation, keep animals from jumping, and provide added safety
- marine animals, such as hermit crabs, fiddler crabs, marine snails, starfish, fish, etc.

Be sure to consult a pet store, college science or marine biology department, or *The Marine Aquarium Reference: Systems and Invertebrates* by Martin A. Moe for complete instructions on how to set up and use this equipment. By establishing a partnership with a local pet store or college, it is often possible to acquire no-cost or reduced-cost equipment and advice.

Additional materials:
- observation journals
- water testing kits (for nitrates and pH levels)
- microscopes and slides
- smaller plastic or glass containers for independent marine animal study

TEACHING TIPS

- The larger the tank, the easier it is to maintain.

Optimum conditions include: (1) temperature of 72°-85° F, (2) pH of 8.0 or higher, (3) hydrometer reading of 1.023, (4) lowest possible nitrates, and (5) lighting of 2 watts per gallon of fluorescent light with blue spectrum.

• The natural substrate should be 1"-2" deep on top of the filter plate.

• Add artificial saltwater, conditioner, and nitrifying bacteria to tank. Let the aquarium run for approximately one week before adding marine animals.

• A properly established marine aquarium is a balanced living system. This balance depends on system inputs and outputs. As in the ocean, both abiotic and biotic factors will influence the aquarium's water chemistry. To successfully establish a marine aquarium, you must have naturally-occurring nitrifying bacteria in the filter media. These bacteria remove poisonous nitrogenous wastes by converting them to less dangerous forms.

• The growth of algae is another indicator of the tank water chemistry. Diatoms, growing along the bottom as a brown mat, will be the first to colonize the tank, followed by blue-green algae. Green algae take over as the tank becomes established and the toxic level of the water decreases.

• Be sure to take advantage of the opportunity to study the nitrogen cycle and natural succession.

• Unlike coastal dwellers, landlocked science teachers cannot run to the seashore to obtain animals to stock an aquarium. Most large biological supply houses will ship live marine animals anywhere in the country. Many pet stores that trade in tropical fish can also supply you with marine animals. Check grocery stores for live oysters, mussels, clams, and lobsters.

• Establishment and maintenance of a marine aquarium are ongoing class projects that provide ample opportunities for whole class and small group investigations. Class discussions are essential to provide students the opportunity to compare findings, to probe student thinking, and stimulate further investigations.

• If funds and/or expertise are not available, consider maintaining and monitoring a freshwater aquarium.

SAFETY CONSIDERATIONS

• When working with the aquarium in the classroom, unplug all electrical equipment before placing a net or your hand into the tank to avoid the possibility of electrical shocks. Saltwater is extremely corrosive and is a good conductor. (Be sure to take advantage of the opportunity to discuss why saltwater is a better conductor than freshwater.) Check, however, that all equipment is plugged back in and turned on after completing your task.

• Avoid placing hands directly into the tank, as body oils, soaps, and lotions contaminate the water. If you wish to observe an animal more closely, place it in a smaller container of water for a short period of time. Return the animal to the tank when the observation is completed. Discard the water in the small container.

PROCEDURE

1. Before setting up the marine aquarium, engage the class in the following discussions and activities about the aquarium environment you are creating: What are some of the kinds of plants and animals that are found in the ocean? What nonliving (abiotic) factors are present? How will a saltwater aquarium be different from a freshwater aquarium?

2. If possible, invite someone from a community pet store, local college, or a state Game and Parks Department to discuss the types of equip-

ment needed to maintain a marine aquarium and its operation. Ask them to specifically address water salinity, temperature, light, and aeration.

3. Have the students help set up the tank and other equipment, condition the tank, and add and feed the animals.

4. Have students keep a journal (notebook) of daily happenings. This can consist of individual or small group observations of specific changes in abiotic and biotic factors that are recorded over an extended period of time. Most observations will fall into three major areas: water chemistry, observations of specific organisms, and interactions among organisms (Spence & Medlicott 1982).

Whole class activities

1. Using water testing kits, have students measure the concentration of different nitrogenous wastes and pH over time. Have students observe whether or not these concentrations change as the tank matures.

2. Have students use a microscope to observe and identify the progression of different types of algae blooms. Students can also observe the link between water quality and the appearance of various forms of algae.

3. Have students examine and compare different animals' individual features, such as coloration (camouflages, countershading, disruptive, false eye spots, advertising, and warning), body shape, appendages, special body features, and behavior. Have them think about what type of habitat and lifestyle that animal is adapted to survive in. How do the features observed enhance its survival? What special problems does the marine animal face to survive?

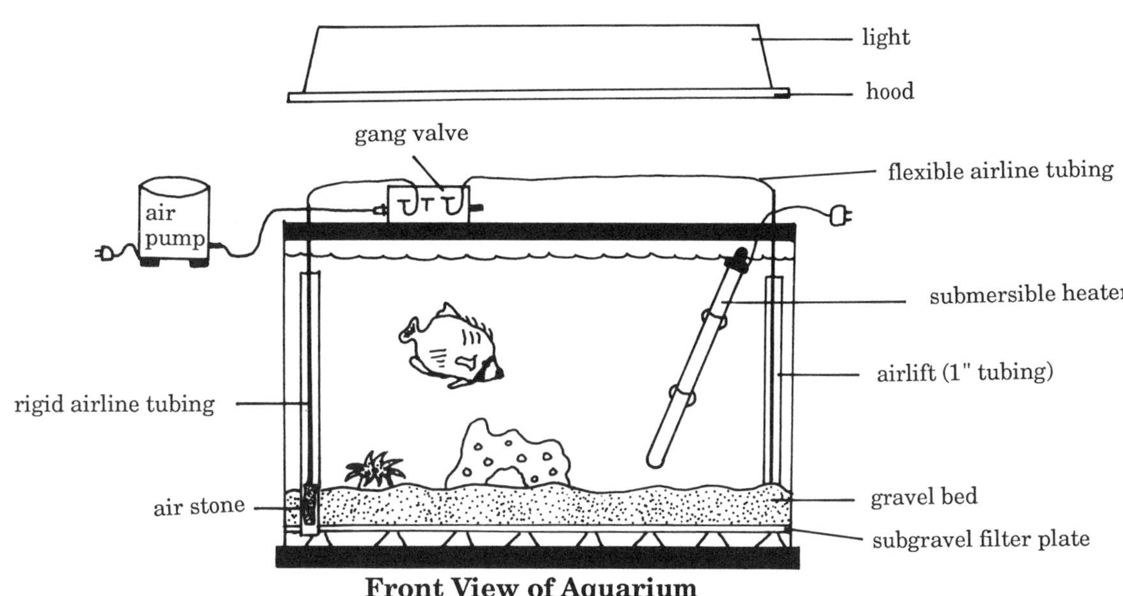

Front View of Aquarium

4. Have students observe animals for specific intervals of time. Have them record behaviors exhibited by a particular animal (i.e., eating; aggression; defense; motion; location in individual containers, such as large glass jars or plastic beverage containers). Be sure to return animals to the main tank when you are through, so they will not die from fouled water.

5. Some animals are hardy enough to be used in manipulations. For instance, hermit crabs can be trained to locate food in a simple T-shaped maze (Spence & Medlicott 1982). The pulling strength of a marine snail can be tested by gluing a string to the shell (using water soluble glue) and attaching varying numbers of paper clips to it. Animal preference for color can be tested by placing different-colored pieces of paper under clear-bottomed observation trays. Crustacean and fish reaction to light can also be tested. Remind students that the animals must be handled gently and immediately returned to the tank if they exhibit any signs of stress.

6. Students should observe the novel way starfish move along the glass of the aquarium. Investigate how this is similar to or different from the method used by sea urchins or other marine animals. Be careful. Moving the starfish when it is attached to the glass will injure the animal by ripping off some of its tube feet (Morholt & Brandwein 1986).

7. Using a separate small tank, have students observe how clams (bivalves) pump water in and out of their bodies. Use an eye dropper to deliver a diluted (1 drop/liter) sample of food coloring in the water near one of the clam's siphons. Which siphon draws water in and which directs water out of the animal (Hampton & Weston 1982)? Have the students also observe the feeding behavior of tubeworms or barnacles (filter feeders). How does it differ from that of the clam?

8. Marine animals can be used to investigate interactive behavior between animals. Have students observe two animals' behavior over time. Which is aggressive or submissive? Do animals differ in their responses? Are any animal interactions helpful to both animals studied? Which animal benefits most from the relationship?

For example, certain kinds of fish may set up territories and defend them. One animal may kill and/or eat another. Crabs are aggressive and may dominate the tank. Some small fish clean parasites from larger fish, and some marine animals form symbiotic relationships.

9. Have students create a food chain/web representative of the marine aquarium. Explain possible plant-and-animal and animal-and-animal relationships.

10. Have the class list what they would like to know about life in a marine aquarium and write their questions on the board. Divide the students into pairs and assign each pair to select one of the class questions (or one of its own) to answer, design a method to answer the chosen question, and perform the investigation. In addition, have each pair of students record a brief description of its investigation, procedure, observations (including sketches, graphs, or tables), and conclusions. Students should include other ideas they would like to explore or other questions they have about life in a marine aquarium. Formal student reports can be written and illustrated with sketches of the animal observed, data graphs, etc.

11. Use class discussions to review group investigations, to find out what the students learned, and to increase student communication and listening skills.

SUMMING UP

A marine aquarium in the classroom provides science teachers with a wonderful resource and inland students with firsthand experience with marine organisms. In addition, due to its diverse components, the marine aquarium can easily be incorporated into a wide range of topics for instruction.

REFERENCES

Hampton, C.H. & Weston, T. (1982). *Marine organisms in the classroom.* (Project CAPTE [teaching module] SC1). Manteo, NC: Dare County Board of Education.

Madrazo, G.M., Jr. & Hounshell, P.B. (1990). *Oceanography for landlocked classrooms.* Reston, VA: National Association of Biology Teachers.

Moe, M.A. (1989). *The marine aquarium reference: Systems and invertebrates.* Plantation, FL: Green Turtle Publications.

Morholt, E. & Brandwein, P.F. (1986). *A sourcebook for the biological sciences.* San Diego: Harcourt Brace Jovanovich.

Spence, L. & Medlicott, J. (1982). *North Carolina marine education manual.* Raleigh, NC: North Carolina State University.

ORIGINAL SOURCES

Balcolm, Nancy Chartier. (1990). Setting up a marine aquarium. In G.M. Madrazo, Jr. & P.B. Hounshell (Eds.), *Oceanography for Landlocked Classrooms* (pp. 18-24). Reston, VA: National Association of Biology Teachers.

Wright, David A. & Wright, Emmett L. (1990). Using marine aquaria. In G.M. Madrazo, Jr. & P.B. Hounshell (Eds.), *Oceanography for Landlocked Classrooms* (pp. 25-28). Reston, VA: National Association of Biology Teachers.

Using Marine Aquaria — Student Activity Report Form

During the next few weeks, you will help set up and stock a marine aquarium in your classroom. Along with the other students in your class, you will also engage in several activities — individually and in groups — that deal with observing this marine ecosystem and the plant and animal life that resides there.

Although the information and observations you gather will not all be the same, as the activities will vary, the following format can be used to report your findings on all the investigations you perform:

1. Name of the activity ______________________________

2. List the materials you used during this activity.

3. Write a brief description of the procedure you used during this investigation.

4. Write a brief description of your findings during this investigation.

5. Draw a sketch, make a graph, or devise a table to visually illustrate your findings.

6. What conclusions can be drawn from performing this activity?

7. List and define any new words you encountered while engaged in this activity.

Songs of Giants: Bioacoustics in Cetaceans

Adapted from an original activity by Karen Travers

The sea is anything but silent. Clicks, snaps, squeaks, croaks, whistles, booms, and moans resound throughout the ocean depths. From the grunts and growls of the ocean sunfish to the foghorn-like blasts of the toad fish, marine animals produce an interesting variety of sounds. Sounds facilitate mating, mark territory, aid navigation, and promote group unity.

The most extraordinarily complex and often hauntingly beautiful sounds are those produced by cetaceans: baleen and toothed whales. For the educator, the study of sound in whales provides an opportunity to capitalize on our natural fascination with this unique group of intelligent mammals while integrating both biology and physics in the classroom.

Whales use sound to communicate and "see" underwater. This provides a fine example of successful adaptation to environmental constraints. Sound communication in marine mammals evolved because it offered significant survival value. Below 150 meters, the sea is dark, making vision almost useless, and surface layers provide only minimal visibility.

A sense of smell is also of limited value since sea water is a poor conductor of scent particles. Sea water, however, is an excellent conductor of sound waves, making sound an efficient method of gathering information.

OBJECTIVES

- Students will estimate the speed of sound.

- Students will create a musical communication pattern.

- Students will investigate whales and other marine mammals.

- Students will present their findings to the class.

- Students will discuss the various adaptations needed by mammals to live in the ocean.

- Students will examine the impact of mankind on sea mammals.

MATERIALS

- blocks of wood
- metric measuring tape
- sound tapes of ocean mammals
- combs
- balloons
- construction paper
- butcher paper
- tissue paper
- markers
- video camera
- research materials
- computers

TEACHING TIPS

- Sound travels at 330 meters per second in air with a temperature of 0° C. The speed increases with increasing temperature. Sound travels at 1,666 meters per second in sea water, about five times faster than in air.

• Interdisciplinary connections can easily be made. In music classes, students can listen to a recording of "Callings" by the Paul Winter Consort and hear how musicians have responded to marine mammal sounds using the jazz mode. Students can then experiment with their own creative expressions.

The math class can examine the size of whales and determine relative proportions. Mathematical connections are also made when estimating the speed of sound.

Social studies connections include researching the history of whaling, use of sonar in World War II, animal geography, the Eskimos' use of whales and the role of whales in their culture, and societal issues that may result in extinctions of various species of sea mammals.

The English class can read *Moby Dick* by Herman Melville and report on their impressions of whaling.

• There are many groups of sea mammals to research, including seals, walruses, dolphins, whales, and manatees. Have your students research specific mammals, such as Humpback whales, sperm whales, bottle-nosed dolphins, right whales, gray whales, bowhead whales, or Orcas.

PROCEDURE

1. Ask students how they typically communicate with one another. Record all responses. Many of the responses will involve the conduction of sound in air.

Ask students how fast sound travels in air and how they can verify the speed given in textbooks. Since the speed of sound can be realistically estimated by making *echoes,* ask students if they know what an "echo" is. Explain that the class is going to make echoes on the school ground, using two blocks of wood and the school building, to try to determine the speed sound travels in air.

Taking the class outdoors, have student volunteers clap the blocks of wood together while the whole class listens for the echo. Explore different locations around the school building to find the best place to stand to produce a good echo. Ask the students to determine how many echoes they hear in 20 seconds. Do several trials and record the answers. Measure the distance the clappers are standing from the school building and use this information to calculate the speed of sound in meters per second.

Does sound travel the same speed in water? If a pool is accessible, have students design and conduct an experiment to determine the speed of sound in water.

2. Play a sound track of sea animals. Ask students to identify the sounds they hear. What kinds of animals would they expect to find in the sea?

The reason why marine animals sing is a subject for speculation. Ask the class why they think these animals sing. Play a whale recording, such as Roger Payne's classic *Songs of the Humpback Whale,* and have the students speculate about the mood or the intent of the whale singing.

If the recording has the calls of more than one whale species, try comparing the vocalizations for complexity, pitch, and duration. Beluga whales, right whales, grays, and Orcas all have distinctly different calls.

As the students listen, have them draw the high and low sound variations as one continuous line on a piece of paper. The results will look similar to sonograms or voice pictures scientists record using underwater hydrophones.

3. Many marine mammals, including dolphins, sperm whales, and some seals examine their

surroundings using directed pulses of sound or *echolocation.* Listening to a recording of a dolphin, it is easy to see how dolphins can use a loud burst of sound to stun or even kill their prey. What are some practical applications for the dolphin's unique echolocation ability? (Hint: Sonar equipment on Navy ships and devices used by the visually impaired.)

Dolphins make a Morse code-like pattern of clicks and whistles, barks and whines, that they use for communication. Dividing the class into groups of three or four, have the students simulate the dolphin's clicks by running their fingernails over combs. Whistles can be made by allowing air to escape from an inflated balloon while the mouthpiece is stretched taut. Ask each group to create a pattern that a dolphin might use to convey a simple message. See if the whole class can decipher each group's message.

4. Have the students select a sea mammal to research. Each student should select one type of sea mammal that he/she would like to learn about from the perspective of the mammal. Encourage creativity. Students can use construction paper, tissue paper, butcher paper, models, computers, etc., to emulate their chosen sea mammals, and present their findings to the class. Videotape student presentations so that class members can review their performances.

5. Discuss similarities of sea mammals. How are sea mammals different from or similar to other mammals? Talk about the various adaptations that are needed for the oceanic ecosystem. Have the class create a possible food web.

6. Compile a list of reasons sea mammals are important to humans. Include both direct products and information learned, such as *voiceprints* and *sonar.* Discuss the impact of mankind on sea mammals. Consider whether or not whaling should be controlled and discuss the effects environmental problems, such as oil spills and global warming, have on sea mammals.

EXTENSIONS

• Visit an aquarium or other marine facility with live marine mammals to observe their behavior and communication firsthand. Which mammals seem to be the most popular with people visiting the aquarium? Ask students how they can find out.

• Explore other methods of communication, such as body language, Braille, sign language, etc. See how many methods can be used to convey simple messages like *danger* or *the location of food.*

• Bats' use of echolocation in the atmosphere is the similar to dolphin echolocation in the ocean. Compare the anatomy, physiology, adaptive complexes, and the problems air and water, respectively, impose on echolocation in both groups of animals.

• Let students explore sound and their own voices using an oscilloscope. Use a guitar or other stringed instrument to explore a pattern of frequency and pitch.

REFERENCES

Bright, M. (1984). *Animal language.* Ithaca, NY: Cornell University Press.

Heintzelman, D.S. (1981). *A world guide to whales, dolphins and porpoises.* Tulsa, OK: Winchester Press.

Lerman, M. (1986). *Marine biology: Environment, diversity, and ecology.* Menlo Park, CA: The Benjamin/Cummings Publishing Company.

Macdonald, D. (Ed.) (1984). *The encyclopedia of mammals.* New York: File Publication.

Miller, F. (1980). *Concepts in physics.* New York: Harcourt Brace Jovanovich.

Minasian, S.M., Balcomb, K.C. & Foster, L. (1984). *The world of whales.* Washington, DC: Smithsonian Books.

Payne, R. (1994). *Among whales.* New York: Macmillan Publishing Company.

Slijper, E.J. (1962). *Whales.* Ithaca, NY: Cornell University Press.

RECORDS

Deep voices: The second whale record. (1977). Hollywood, CA: Capitol Records.

Payne, R. (1970). *Songs of the Humpback whale.* Hollywood, CA: Capitol Records.

Sounds of sea animals. (1959). New York, NY: Folkways Science Series FX 6125.

Winter, P. (1980). *Callings.* Litchfield, CT: Living Music Records.

VIDEOS

Other sources include National Geographic films featuring the explorations of Jacques Cousteau.

ORIGINAL SOURCE

Travers, Karen. (1990). Songs of giants: Bioacoustics in Cetaceans. In G.M. Madrazo, Jr. & P.B. Hounshell (Eds.), *Oceanography for Landlocked Classrooms* (pp. 41-45). Reston, VA: National Association of Biology Teachers.

Chapter 3
Food Explorations

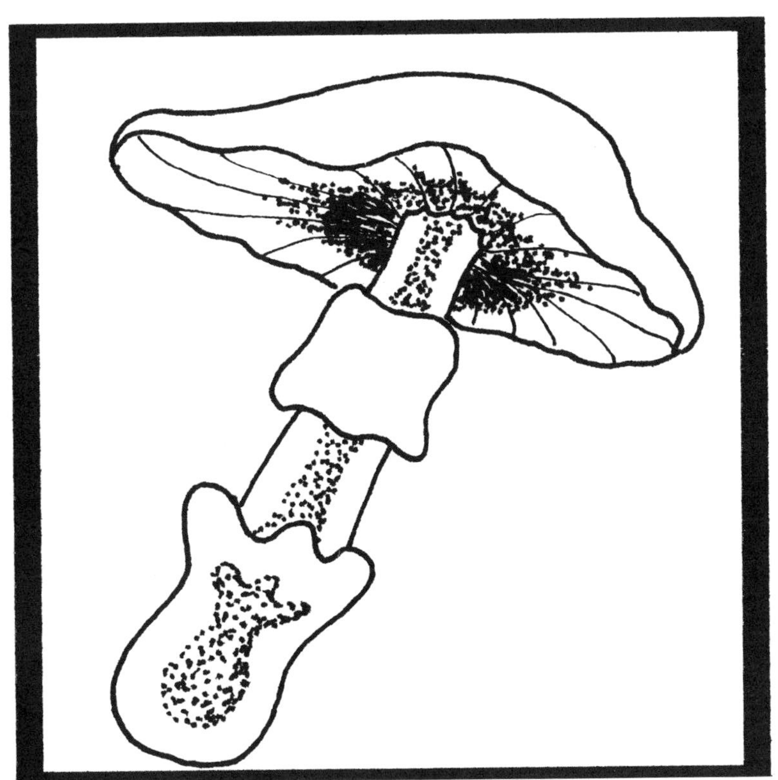

Pizza Analogy

Adapted from an original activity by Barbara Cauchon

This activity was created to counteract the students' cries of "I'm NOT an artist!" whenever they are asked to create a diagram. The purpose of this exercise is to teach students basic drawing skills and proper diagram format, both of which will be used throughout the rest of the year.

The activity also introduces the concept of field of view and its relationship to magnification. Students do this activity right in their lab notebooks and are encouraged to take notes so that they may refer back to them during future labs.

OBJECTIVES

- Students will practice some basic drawing techniques.

- Students will know what is expected of them when making laboratory diagrams.

- Students will explain the relationship between magnification and the area of the field of view.

MATERIALS

- 35 mm slides of an uncooked pizza
- slide projector and screen
- overhead projector, blank transparencies, markers
- 35 mm camera and film or digital camera
- lab notebooks
- pencils
- rulers or straight edges

TEACHING TIPS

- Young people love pizza, and so an activity that features this teenage favorite provides a natural connection between the concept of diagram drawing being studied and the lives of students in the class.

Many students have made positive comments about this activity. It gives them confidence in their own abilities and knowledge about what the teacher expects a diagram to contain. With proper explanation, "Pizza Analogy" techniques can be used in many different biology and life science classes.

- This activity is done toward the beginning of the school year before doing microscope work. It will help to do a fair amount of microscope work after the pizza drawing lab to reinforce the techniques learned and give students additional feedback.

- If the use of food is problematic, long distance and closeup shots of a forest also work well.

- A three-ring binder works especially well for a student laboratory notebook. This allows drawings to be done on unlined paper and for papers to be turned in, graded, and included in the notebook for future reference.

- A rubric for assessing student performance of the assigned drawings is included on the student handout at the end of this activity.

- The book, *Drawing on the Right Side of the*

Brain, by Betty Dawson may give teachers more ways to help students gain skills and confidence in their drawing abilities.

PROCEDURE

1. The teacher will need to make 35 mm slides of a pizza before doing this activity. A homemade pizza loaded with toppings that will show up well in photographs, including pepperoni slices, onion rings, anchovies, sun dried tomatoes, broccoli pieces, artichoke hearts, mushrooms, etc., works well for this exercise. Take several shots of the pizza using a 35 mm camera with flash loaded with slide film or a digital camera.

2. To simulate the difference in field of view for the students, take a photograph with the camera far enough away so that the entire perimeter of the pizza is shown. Then take another closer shot so that the images are larger, but the perimeter is no longer visible. Take several pictures at each distance.

3. The day of the lab, set up the overhead projector next to the slide projector. The slide projector is loaded with pizza slides. Each projector is set up so that both will project their images on the screen simultaneously. The students should have their lab notebooks, pencils, and straight edges ready before beginning.

4. Introduce the activity by explaining that you do not consider yourself an artist but that you have learned some helpful drawing techniques from a friend who is an artist that you would like to share with the class. Go on to say that, during the activity, you will explain the format the students will be using whenever they draw in class.

Pass out the "Pizza Analogy — Procedure for the Student" pages and ask the class members to attach them to their notebooks for future reference. Go through the directions with the students, doing the activity with them by making a drawing on the overhead projector.

5. Using the student directions as a guide (see the worksheet following this activity), turn on the projectors and explain that the class is going to draw a pizza, with the analogy of the pizza being somewhat like a microscopic organism that the students may be asked to draw in the future. Walk them through the directions for setting up their field of vision boundaries, adding crosshatches as guides, and beginning their drawings, while simultaneously making a sample drawing on the overhead.

6. After going through the first quadrant, let them continue on their own, circulating among the students, offering support and suggestions. It is important to offer encouragement during this time to build student confidence in their abilities, no matter how primitive the drawing. Assure them that, with practice, they will all improve.

7. The teacher may then choose to show the difference between powers of magnification and visible field of view. Using both the long and close photographs of the same pizza in the projector, explain that the move from "low power" to "high power" can be simulated by moving between slides. Refer to the long shot of the pizza as a simulation of 100X and the close shot as a simulation of 400X. This is a wonderful visual tool to illustrate a concept that often confuses students during microscope use. Reinforce this concept when students begin actual microscope work by reminding them of the difference in the portion of the pizza they could see during this activity.

8. After completing the activity, further drawing exercises may be assigned, perhaps for homework, to give students more practice in diagram drawing. The more they practice, the better they will get!

EXTENSION

Students can gain further experience with diagrams by creating drawings of other subjects. Have students choose their own subjects from nature to draw and label, such as leaves. Tell students to make their drawings as accurate and true-to-life as possible. Extra credit may be given if the students draw separate diagrams of their subject at the two powers of magnification discussed in class (100X and 400X).

ORIGINAL SOURCE

Cauchon, Barbara. (1993). The pizza lab. In L.R. Sanders (Ed.), *Favorite Labs from Outstanding Teachers — Volume II* (pp. 106-109). Reston, VA: National Association of Biology Teachers.

DIAGRAM INFORMATION AND PROCEDURE

1. Rubric for evaluating student diagrams:

Criteria	Proficient	Basic	In Progress
Title	Each diagram has a title in the upper right-hand corner that is underlined indicating what has been drawn.	Each diagram has a title.	Titles are not used.
Magnification	Magnification power is correctly indicated for each drawing.	Magnification is indicated on most of the drawings.	No magnification power is given.
Labeling	Labels are straight and placed on the horizontal.	Labels are straight but are not horizontal.	Labels are used but lines are crossed and labels are haphazardly placed.
Handwriting and spelling	All labels are legible and spelled correctly.	Most of the labels are legible and spelled correctly.	Many labels are illegible and misspelled.
Mechanics	Used unlined white paper and pencil.	Pencil is used on lined paper or pen or colored markers are used on white paper.	Pen or colored markers and lined paper are used.

2. Starting the diagram:

• If making observations using a microscope, first draw a circle to represent the field of vision. This is the area seen when looking through the microscope. Choose a round object to trace the field of vision (petri dish, bottom of beaker, quarter, etc.) — just make sure that the size chosen reflects the amount of material being drawn. In the case of the pizza diagram, simply draw a square.

• Drawing lightly with a pencil, place a set of crosshatches over the area drawn to represent the field of vision. This will help orient you to the subject as drawing begins.

• What is the overall outline of the specimen? Is it round, oval, or irregular? Does it have a centralized body with limbs? Look at the outline of the specimen and ignore the details within; in the case of the pizza, the outline of the low-power pizza is a clean circle.

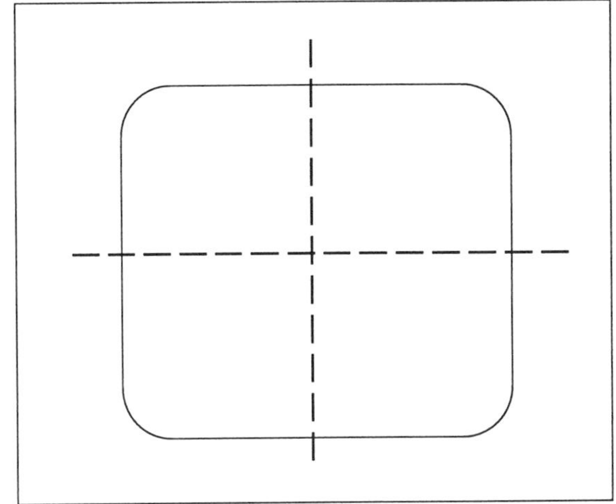

• Imagine that the specimen has a set of crosshatches drawn through it just like the ones traced onto the paper. (Students are now going to try to draw the outline of the specimen one quarter at a time.) Do not worry about the details inside at this time. The crosshatches, both imaginary and drawn, should help.

• Starting at the upper right quadrant, start to draw the outline of the specimen. Continue drawing the outline down to the lower right quadrant, over to the lower left quadrant, then finish in the upper left quadrant. The sketch should look like the specimen that is being drawn. Erase and start again if there are mistakes. Work carefully and relax!

• Observe the outline of the specimen more closely. Is it thicker or darker than the rest of the specimen? If so, darken and thicken the outline on the paper. If not, leave the outline alone. Does the outline have any projections (like hair or cilia)? Look at the drawn outline carefully to make sure it is the best representation of the specimen's outline before moving on to the next page. In the case of the pizza, the outline is thicker and darker, so adjust the drawing accordingly.

3. Details of the drawing:

• Now focus attention on the area inside the outline of the specimen. Take a careful look. Are there smaller objects? What are their sizes and shapes? Are they dark or light in color? In the case of the pizza, look at the different things baked on it. There are irregular-shaped broccoli pieces; long, thin anchovies; clean, circular sausage pieces, etc.

• Starting at the upper right quadrant, start to draw in any details seen inside the specimen. Position the details using the crosshatches. If something is round, draw a circle to represent it in the appropriate place. If it looks thin and hairlike, draw the shape accordingly. Then move on to any other shaped objects.

• Once the upper right quadrant is filled, move to the lower right quadrant and do the same. Continue this until the entire drawing has been filled with detail.

• Now, look at the entire specimen. Are there areas of detail that are darker than others? Darken those on the diagram. Are there areas that are less dark? Lightly darken them in, keeping them lighter than the darkest details. Continue shading in the details, using the specimen as a whole to guide you. In the case of the pizza, the sun-dried tomatoes are the darkest; the broccoli is a bit lighter; the anchovies and sausage a bit lighter still, etc.

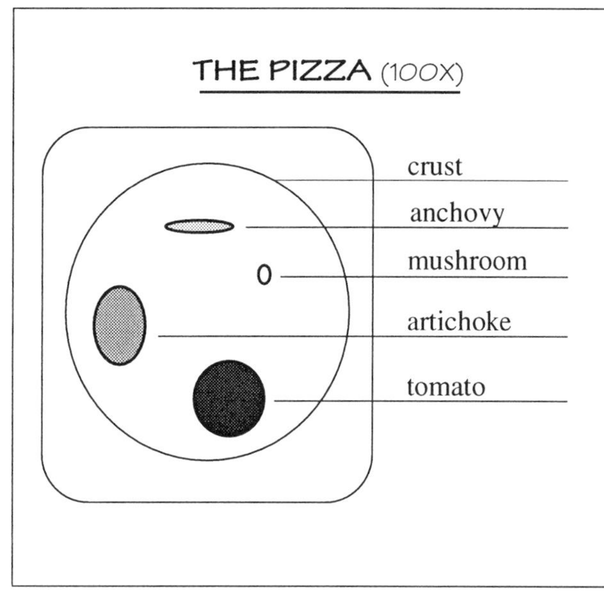

• After drawing in and shading the details, look at the drawing carefully, and then look at the specimen. Is there anything that should be added, redrawn, or erased to make it more clear?

4. Labels and title:

• After drawing the diagram, label any parts that can be identified. Usually a lab that includes drawing a diagram will have a series of parts to be found, drawn, and labeled on the specimen.

• For each part labeled, find a good representation of the part and draw a horizontal, straight line (using a ruler) from the part to an area outside of the diagram (outside the field of view if it is a microscope drawing being done)

• On or to the right of the line, write the name of the part. Write it clearly and make sure the spelling is correct!

• Do this for each part being labeled. Never cross the lines of labels. This causes a great deal of confusion. Also, be sure to indicate a magnification power if a microscope is used for the drawing.

• When all the parts required have been labeled, be sure to give the diagram a title. Underline the title, using a straight edge.

Pizza Lab Requirements Checklist

(Complete before handing in the lab)

✔ Two drawings of the pizza slides should be completed — one of a low magnification and one of a high magnification. **Be sure all drawings have titles and that the magnification power is indicated!**

✔ The following parts should have been labeled: *pan, onion, anchovy, artichoke heart, sausage slices, pepper, broccoli, sun-dried tomato, crust, and pepperoni slices.*

✔ On a separate sheet of paper, answer the following questions. Hand this sheet in with your completed drawings.

1. During the pizza lab, the move from low power of magnification was simulated. Describe how this change in magnification affected what you saw of the pizza.

2. How would this affect a diagram of a group of cells when drawing them using both 100X and 400X during a lab activity?

The Fungi Feast

Adapted from an original activity by Kevin Collins

The Fungi Feast is a series of activities for a unit on fungi. The purpose of these activities is to emphasize the positive role that fungi has in students' lives. The primary focus of this series is on a fermentation investigation; however, as the fermentation process continues, students will also turn their attention to bread making, mushrooms, and the production of cheese.

OBJECTIVES

- Students will formulate a hypothesis.

- Students will design and conduct a fermentation investigation to test that hypothesis.

- Students will explore the role of yeast in bread making.

- Students will examine mushrooms and discover their spores.

- Students will experience fungi in their everyday lives.

- Students will demonstrate the interrelationship of fungi and other organisms by creating food chains and food webs.

MATERIALS

- sugar
- root beer extract
- yeast
- warm water
- one-liter plastic bottles with lids
- microscopes (optional)
- bread dough ingredients: yeast, milk, sugar, shortening, salt, flour, and water
- bread making machines (optional)
- bread pans
- oven
- mushrooms
- plain white paper
- bowl
- hair spray
- variety of cheeses: Roquefort, Brie, Stilton, Camembert, etc.
- crackers
- paper towels
- small paper cups

TEACHING TIPS

- Root beer extract can be found in the spice aisle of large grocery stores. Hires® brand root beer extract and Schilling® brand root beer concentrates have both been used with good results. The Hires® product has been found to make a slightly better tasting root beer. Sassafras roots can also be used to make root beer.

- **Do not** use a glass container when making the root beer. Pressure from the buildup of carbon dioxide may cause the bottle to explode. Plastic bottles tend to stretch with pressure and are less likely to burst. Fill the bottles two-thirds full and cap tightly. Lay the bottles on their sides and place a drip pan under the lids.

- Clean all table tops and lab counters thoroughly. Store all chemicals in secure storage cabinets to avoid accidental poisoning.

• It takes at least one week for the yeast to carbonate the beverage. While the fermentation process is in progress, students can explore other examples of the positive influence of fungi. Several activities are provided.

• Work out an arrangement with either the family and consumer science (previously known as "home economics") teacher or personnel from the school kitchen to use their oven.

• Yeasts are unicellular fungi that reproduce by budding. They reproduce very quickly when provided moisture, a food source, and a warm temperature. As the yeast cells break down their food source, sugar, carbon dioxide is released. It is the carbon dioxide that gives soda pop its fizz.

• Mushrooms are fungi that reproduce through the production of spores. The color of the mushroom spores can make identification of mushrooms easier.

• A basic cheese can be easily made and safely tested by adding 30 ml buttermilk to 950 ml milk. The bacteria normally found in buttermilk will break down the sugar in milk, forming lactic acid. Refrigerate at 28° C for 48 hours. Filter through a cheese cloth. Allow the curds two more days of aging in the refrigerator before sampling. The process changes the taste and texture of the milk. The resulting cheese is soft and rather bland tasting. This activity introduces how cheese is made; however, please note that bacterial fermentation is used rather than fungal.

• Interdisciplinary connections include having students design a marketing strategy for their product. This should include designing a label and creating an advertisement for television, radio, or the newspaper. As part of the marketing plan, students will also calculate the cost of the making the product and decide what price to charge the public in order to make a profit (profit margin). They will examine how statistics are used in product comparisons and determine the geographic distribution of major soda brands. Moreover, issues involved with foreign trade, such as the effects of trade restrictions and barriers, tariffs, and the impact of cultural differences and taste differences, will be explored. A connection can also be made to our historical past by having students research how the early settlers made root beer from sassafras roots.

PROCEDURE

1. Introduce the activity by blind tasting popular cola and soft drink products. Tally the data and determine the class' favorite. Ask the students if they have ever wondered how these products are made. Read the product labels to determine ingredients. Tell the class that they are going to make root beer. Ask if they have any idea how to begin. Record student suggestions.

2. Tell the students that the four essential ingredients are water, sugar, yeast, and extract. Divide the class into teams of two students each. Give each team 10 days to produce the best root beer possible. A recipe is included with the commercial root beer extract.

Brainstorm possible variables that would make a difference in the taste of the root beer. For example, would adding additional sugar make the root beer sweeter, or would adding more extract give the root beer a stronger root beer taste? Would using a sugar substitute such as saccharide (many times sweeter than table sugar) make a difference? Each team chooses the variable it wishes to investigate, formulates a hypothesis, and designs and conducts the experiment, producing a its own root beer product.

3. While the student root beer experiments are fermenting, introduce another use of yeast by bringing out all the ingredients for making bread. Ask the students to help combine all the ingredients except for the yeast. Ask students

what they think the effect will be of adding yeast to the mixture. Record student responses on the board. Add the dissolved yeast to half the bread dough and set the mixture aside.

Have the class members examine yeast cells under the microscope. Discuss what they saw.

After a short time (10-15 minutes), call student attention back to the two dough mixtures and ask, "What has happened? Why?" The difference between the two mixtures is that the bread dough with yeast added to it has begun to rise. The yeast broke down the sugar into ethyl alcohol, carbon dioxide, and energy (heat). Carbon dioxide normally exists as a gas, and since most gas molecules are moving quickly and are able to escape a confined area, the action of carbon dioxide bubbles moving upward made the bread dough rise. The dough without yeast added did not rise. Ask the class why they think the bread doesn't taste like alcohol. Tell the students that the alcohol evaporates during baking.

Bake the two mixtures. Have the students taste and compare. Look for holes where the carbon dioxide has escaped.

4. Bring a variety of cheeses produced using fungi into class for the students to study. Some suggested cheeses are Roquefort (bleu cheese), Brie, Stilton, and Camembert. Distribute some crackers and cheese for students to taste. Have the class microscopically examine the blue granules of blue cheese. Ask the students what they see and how they think blue cheese is made. How is this different from how other cheese is made?

5. Have the students examine and taste mushrooms. Place students in groups of three to research one othe the following topics: the different kinds of mushrooms, uses of mushrooms, conditions necessary to grow mushrooms, how mushrooms reproduce, where mushrooms are found, mushroom farms, the commercial aspects of mushrooms, etc. Have the student groups present their findings to the class.

If possible, collect wild mushrooms. Carefully remove the stems and place the mushroom cap (gill side down) on a white sheet of paper. Cover with a bowl overnight. (Do **NOT** eat the wild mushrooms, for although some are edible, many are poisonous.) Carefully uncover and remove the mushroom cap the next morning and examine the spore print design on the paper. The prints can be preserved by spraying them with hair spray. Mushrooms reproduce by spores, and the colors of the spores aid in mushroom identification.

6. Have students research other examples and uses of fungi. Symbiotic relationships and decomposition (including recycling of nutrients) may be explored. Create food chains and food webs to demonstrate the interrelationships between organisms and fungi. This may also be a good opportunity to introduce the negative effects of fungi by examining bread mold. See "Extensions" for additional suggestions concerning molds.

7. After the root beer has been fermenting for eight days, conduct blind taste tests in class to determine the students' favorite root beer. Discuss the different variables used by each team and their effects on taste and the purposes of sugar, the extract, and the yeast in the root beer making process.

8. Summarize the different kinds of fungi discussed in this series of activities and how each kind is beneficial in everyday life.

EXTENSIONS

• The process used by the yeast to break down the sugar is called "fermentation." Explore other examples of fermentation. Research Pasteur's connection to fermentation.

• When yeast cells break down nutrients in the absence of oxygen, energy is produced as well as carbon dioxide and ethyl alcohol. More carbon dioxide is released as the rate of fermentation increases. Explore what factors might affect the rate of fermentation (temperature, time, substrate concentration and type, etc.). Pour equal amounts of yeast solution and sugar solution into 10-ml calibrated pipettes whose tips are sealed with floral clay. Insert a 16x125-mm test tube. Invert both quickly. Record readings in five-minute intervalS. Analyze the results and discuss the concepts/ideas that would transfer to other organisms.

• The activities in the previous activities have all stressed the positive aspects of fungi. Fungi also affect our lives in a negative manner. This can be explored by having students examine and draw bread mold. The students can then design and conduct investigations to determine the best conditions for bread mold growth.

• The students can also determine if mold will grow on other food by placing various bits of food into individual plastic bags with a damp paper towel. Let a little air into the bag and securely close each one. Do NOT open the bags. Ask the students to describe the mold they see growing on each food sample, noting any differences in color or appearance. Do different molds grow on different foods?

SUMMING UP

There are many different kinds of fungi. The principal role of fungi is to decompose and recycle living material. Fungi also benefit humans in other ways. Probably one of the most well-known fungi is the *Penicillium* mold used to produce **penicillin**, an important antibiotic.

Some fungi, such as mushrooms, are a food source, and others play a vital role in producing such foods as cheese, crackers, bread, and even lemon drops. Yeast are now being used in genetic engineering experiments. This variety of roles makes fungi an essential component of the food chain and the world around us.

ORIGINAL SOURCE

Collins, Kevin. (1993). The fungi feast. In L.R. Sanders (Ed.), *Favorite Labs from Outstanding Teachers — Volume II* (pp. 100-101). Reston, VA: National Association of Biology Teachers.

Food for Thought

Adapted from an original activity by Susan K. Johnson

Students often memorize information without understanding it. One of the reasons that this occurs in life science classes is that students have had little previous experience with basic biological concepts and, therefore, find them abstract and difficult to understand. In this activity, the familiar becomes a model that can be used to help students construct meaning for a concept that often is difficult to learn. It can also be used to help students construct meaning for terms that may be commonly used but often misunderstood.

"Food for Thought" is a good activity to introduce a unit on heredity. In this exercise, a familiar example that students can relate to will be used to explain the unfamiliar. The familiar, in this case, are cookies and cookie recipes, while the unfamiliar are the biological concept of heredity and the supporting ideas of environment, genotype, phenotype, adaptation, evolution, continuity, diversity, and mutation.

OBJECTIVES

- Students will bake cookies using one of the four recipes listed on the work sheets following this activity.

- Students will be able to distinguish between "genotype" and "phenotype."

- Students will discuss continuity and diversity.

- Students will generate examples of the effect of the environment on phenotype.

- Students will describe how mutations occur.

- Students will develop analogies to express their knowledge of heredity.

MATERIALS

- ingredients for four (4) cookie recipes
- cookie sheets
- ovens
- paper plates
- napkins
- paper cups
- milk
- cookies
- "Procedure for the Student" worksheets
- "Questions for the Baker" worksheets
- "Discussion Questions" worksheets

TEACHING TIPS

- As teenagers are often known to consume milk by the gallon, use small paper cups (3-6 ounces). It is recommended that the teacher pour the milk to prevent distribution problems.

- Although a majority of students may wish to make a particular recipe, such as the ever-popular chocolate chip cookie, each of the four recipes should be equally represented.

- Timing of the activity is important. It can be done in two class periods — one to bake the cookies and another to observe and discuss the results. However, the pace is critical. If you have to rush through the discussion, the objectives of the activity will not be accomplished. Allow ample time for students to generate questions. Having some time during a third class period for further discussion may be helpful in facilitating in-depth consideration of all the concepts included in this exercise.

• The value of this activity increases exponentially as it is adapted to a particular classroom. One variation of the activity that has already been tried is to ask a separate group of students to bake one of the recipes but to add only half of the recommended amount of an assigned ingredient — or to leave an assigned ingredient out entirely. These changes in the amounts of certain ingredients can vary from not being very "harmful" to being "lethal," depending on their importance to the "survival" of the cookie.

• It is possible to use commercially prepared cookie dough. However, making the cookies from scratch gives the students some experience with measuring. The mathematical aspect of the exercise can be extended by asking students to adjust the recipe by a specified proportion (make half of the recipe, triple the recipe, etc.).

PROCEDURE

Before the activity:

1. As a part of the activity, the students are given the assignment to bake one of four cookie recipes. If at all possible, arrange to use the home economics room. Assign the students to teams of four. The students should be responsible for measuring, mixing, baking, and cleaning up.

2. The students are asked to fill out the "Questions for the Baker" at the time the cookies are made and bring the completed worksheet to class along with the baked cookies. The questions on the worksheet are designed to allow the recording of data that may prove useful in answering the "Discussion Questions" during the classroom portion of the activity.

Day of the activity:

1. It is recommended that the activity be done in small groups of 2-4 students. Working on the questions within a group helps to establish a favorable climate and expands the potential for ideas and interpretations that are later shared with the entire class.

2. At the beginning of the activity, each student group should put its cookies on a plate and then place the plate with the group of plates containing cookies baked from the same recipe. The four different groups of cookies can be situated around the room during Part I so that there will not be too many students working in one area. Groups of three or four students can move from one kind of cookie to another and record observations in their notebooks. Following observation, the student groups will be given time to discuss their answers while filling out Part I of the "Discussion Questions."

3. After about 5-10 minutes, the groups can begin Part II. To do so, each group should get an empty plate and collect one cookie from each of the plates of cookies. They can find a place to sit and work on the questions in Part II. This is a good time to pass out the cups and pour the milk. The student groups can enjoy the cookies and milk while they work on Part II questions.

4. About 15 minutes should be allowed for the groups to work on the Part II questions. Instruct them to use their time wisely so that they are not left with most of the questions and only a few minutes in which to answer them. The rest of the class period can then be used for the whole class to discuss their answers.

5. Have students create their own analogies.

POINTS FOR DISCUSSION

The following points should be emphasized during the time allotted for class discussion:

1. The ingredients of the four recipes have been selected for specific reasons. For example, the two cookies (oatmeal raisin and oatmeal chocolate chip) that have the most similar appearances *(phenotypes)* actually differ the most in terms of their recipes' genetic makeups *(genotypes)*. The relationship of having a similar appearance and very different recipe is analogous to the relationship between the black bear and the panda bear. In appearance, both bears look similar. However, each has a very different DNA "recipe." Students should be asked to state other instances in nature that illustrate this point.

2. There are many different kinds of cookies. Just look at how many different kinds of cookies there are in the cookie aisle of a grocery store! This diversity provides us with a lot of choices and is similar to the great diversity of organisms. *Diversity* is due to the different recipes used to make the cookies. While cookies made with the same recipe look very similar, there are still some differences. What are some of the differences? (Some cookies are larger or smaller than others; some are flat; some are thick; some have smooth edges; and others have an irregular edge). Recipes are often passed down from generation to generation with few, if any, changes. If the same cookie recipe is used, cookies will result that are very much alike. This *continuity* also occurs in families. Discuss "continuity" and "variation" in families.

3. The oven temperature (environment) for each recipe did not vary. What happens if the temperature is higher? Lower? *(The environment does influence phenotype. For example, Siamese cats have a genotype for dark-colored fur that is best expressed at a temperature below body temperature.)* Where do you see dark coloring on Siamese cats? *(Ears, nose, paws, and tail.)* What do you think happens if we shave the hair off of the belly of a Siamese cat and cover it with an ice pack? *(You are right! The hair grows back dark.)* The environment also affects our DNA recipe. *(For example, even though a person has the DNA to be tall, if proper nutrition is not available, he or she will not be tall.)* Identical twins have exactly the same genotype and are often studied to determine the effect of environment on phenotype. What differences do you notice between identical twins?

4. What happens if you substitute applesauce for margarine or honey for sugar? What if you leave the sugar out or add an extra cup of sugar? These changes in the recipe are similar to changes that can occur in DNA. Sometimes part of the DNA is lost or deleted from the recipe.

For instance, phenylketonuria (PKU) occurs when a segment of DNA is missing or is defective. The missing DNA is needed to produce an enzyme. Lack of this enzyme can cause brain damage. To prevent the damage from occurring, early testing for the disorder is recommended, followed by a special diet for those who are affected.

Sometimes a piece of DNA is added or a piece is substituted. For example, sickle-cell anemia is due to a substitution. The result is irregularly shaped blood cells that cannot carry adequate oxygen so the affected person feels tired and suffers from anemia.

At other times, a change in the recipe produces a cookie that is better tasting than the original. Beneficial changes in the DNA of living organisms can also occur. For instance, a change in DNA may result in a color change in an organism that improves its chances for survival in a specific environment. Striped or variegated tulips are the result of a change in DNA. These tulips brighten many flower gardens and have become quite popular. Can you think of any other examples?

Changes in DNA or mutations occur naturally. Environmental factors that harm DNA are called *mutagens*. Known mutagens include excessive sunlight, cigarette tars, asbestos, and radioactivity. Discuss some of the toxic and hazardous wastes that are a problem in your area.

5. Following the discussion, summarize the analogies that have been made by making a chart on the overhead or the board. Start by providing an example and then asking the students to fill in the chart. A sample appears below.

SUMMING UP

Many life science teachers have experienced frustration when, at the end of a well-planned unit on genetics, the students are still confused about the meaning of heredity and basic ideas. The value of the analogy becomes evident when it helps students construct meanings for concepts that are unfamiliar to their daily experiences and, therefore, difficult to understand.

ORIGINAL SOURCE

Johnson, Susan K. (1993). Food for thought — The cookie analogy. In L.R. Sanders (Ed.), *Favorite Labs from Outstanding Teachers — Volume II* (pp. 110-116). Reston, VA: National Association of Biology Teachers.

SAMPLE CHART

Familiar Item	*Analogous Term*
Cookies	Heredity
Recipe	DNA
Oven temperature	Effect of environment
Ingredients	Genotype
Appearance	Phenotype
Change	Mutation
Different kinds of cookies	Diversity
Same recipe = similar cookies	Continuity

Food for Thought — Procedure for the Student

Each class member is assigned to a team to bake cookies, following one of the four recipes provided. While making the cookies, answer the questions on the "Questions for the Baker" work sheet given to you by your teacher. The following day, bring the work sheet and cookies to class, as both of these items will be helpful in answering the "Discussion Questions" on the work sheet you will be given that day.

<u>Recipe #1</u>

2 1/4 cups all purpose flour
1 teaspoon baking soda
1 teaspoon salt
1 cup margarine or butter
3/4 cup sugar
3/4 cup firmly packed brown sugar
1 teaspoon vanilla
2 eggs
1 package (12 oz.) chocolate chips

Preheat oven to 375° F. Beat together margarine, sugar, brown sugar, and vanilla until creamy. Beat in eggs. Combine flour, baking soda, and salt. Gradually add to margarine mixture. Stir in chocolate chips. Drop by rounded teaspoonfuls onto ungreased cookie sheets. Bake for 8-11 minutes.

<u>Recipe #2</u>

1 1/2 cups all purpose flour
1 teaspoon baking soda
1 teaspoon salt
1 teaspoon cinnamon
1/4 teaspoon nutmeg
1 1/4 cups margarine or butter
1/2 cup sugar
3/4 cup firmly packed brown sugar
1 teaspoon vanilla
1 egg
3 cups oats
1 cup raisins

Preheat oven to 375° F. Beat together margarine, sugar, and brown sugar until creamy. Beat in egg and vanilla. Combine flour, baking soda, salt, cinnamon, and nutmeg. Gradually add to margarine mixture. Stir in oats and raisins. Drop by rounded teaspoonfuls onto ungreased cookie sheets. Bake 8-11 minutes.

<u>Recipe #3</u>

1 1/2 cups all purpose flour
1 teaspoon baking soda
1 teaspoon salt

$1\frac{1}{4}$ cups margarine or butter
$\frac{1}{2}$ cup sugar
$\frac{3}{4}$ cup firmly packed brown sugar
1 teaspoon vanilla
1 egg
3 cups oats
1 package (12 oz.) chocolate chips

Preheat oven to 375° F. Beat together margarine, sugar, and brown sugar until creamy. Beat in egg and vanilla. Combine flour, baking soda, and salt. Gradually add to margarine mixture. Stir in oats and chocolate chips. Drop by rounded teaspoonfuls onto ungreased cookie sheets. Bake 8-11 minutes.

Recipe #4
$2\frac{3}{4}$ cups all purpose flour
2 teaspoons cream of tartar
1 teaspoon baking soda
$\frac{1}{2}$ teaspoon salt
1 cup shortening, margarine, or butter
$1\frac{1}{2}$ cups sugar
2 eggs

Preheat oven to 350° F. Beat together margarine and sugar. Beat in eggs. Combine flour, cream of tartar, baking soda, and salt. Gradually add to margarine mixture. Roll into balls the size of walnuts. Roll into a mixture of 3 tablespoons sugar and 2 teaspoons cinnamon. Bake 12-15 minutes.

Food for Thought — Questions for the Baker

Group Members ____________________

Date ____________________

1. What recipe (Number One, Two, Three, or Four) were you assigned? ____________________
2. What brand of flour did you use? ____________________
3. Was the flour bleached or unbleached? ____________________
4. Did you use shortening, margarine, or butter? ____________________
5. What was the brand name of the item listed in #4 above? ____________________
6. Did the shortening, margarine, or butter you used come from an animal or vegetable source?

   ____
7. If you used vanilla, was it real or artificial? ____________________
8. Were the eggs small, medium, large, or extra large? ____________________
9. What brand of sugar did you use? ____________________
10. What information about the degree of granulation, if any, was printed on the sugar package?

    ____
11. If you used oats, chocolate chips, or raisins, what brand and/or type did you use?
    - oats ____________________
    - chocolate chips ____________________
    - raisins ____________________
12. How long did you bake the cookies? ____________________
13. Did you vary the recipe in any way? ____________________
14. If you answered yes to #13, what variation did you make? ____________________

Food for Thought — Discussion Questions

Group Members ____

Date ____

PART I

Arrange your cookies on the plate provided by your teacher and put the plate next to the other plates of cookies baked from the same recipe. Resist temptation and refrain from eating any cookies until you are otherwise instructed. Working in your group, answer the questions in Part I and have one person from your group record the answers. Wait until all groups have had a chance to answer the questions in Part I before going on to Part II.

1. Compare the plates of cookies. Do all the cookies on any given plate look identical?

2. What similarities, if any, do you observe?

3. What differences, if any, do you observe?

4. Compare the plates of cookies made from the same recipe. Are the cookies identical from plate to plate?

5. What similarities, if any, do you observe?

6. What differences, if any, do you observe?

PART II

Each group should obtain an empty plate. Place one cookie from every one of the plates of cookies on the new plate. Find a place in the room where you can continue to make cookie observations. Working in your group, answer the questions in Part II. Have one person from your group record your answers. As you work on the questions, feel free to begin an in-depth analysis of the cookies on your plate.

1. What are possible reasons why all the cookies baked by the same team might not be identical?

2. What are possible reasons why all the cookies baked by different teams, using the same recipe, might not be identical? (HINT: Think about the variables involved.)

3. Is there more than one recipe in existence for chocolate chip cookies? Why or why not?

4. Using the cookies as examples, can you always tell by looking at a group of different organisms which had the most similar "recipes"? Explain your answer.

5. Why isn't there only one recipe for cookies?

6. How might recipes come to change from one generation of bakers to the next?

7. How could the recipe be changed to be nutritionally beneficial? Give reasons for your answer.

8. Can you think of cookies that seem to be specific to one ethnic group or geographical location? If yes, give an example.

9. Why might this be?

10. If you were asked to divide these four representatives of the cookie species on the plate into three groups, such as we divide species into varieties or breeds, what would these groups be?

11. What was your rationale for grouping the cookies on the plate the way that you did?

12. Which recipe was the most different from the others? What made it seem different?

(When the groups have finished the cookie questions, we will get back together as a class to share our thoughts.)

The Fruit Lab

Adapted from an original activity by Mary R. Chappell

Dehydration of common fruits is used as the motivating activity to begin a study of fruits. This lab involves student examination of various fruits to note differences and similarities. Expert groups are used to help develop student understanding and appreciation of the role of fruits. Analysis of the fruits helps students to predict how seeds of various fruits are distributed.

This is an interactive lesson in which small groups of students work for several minutes and then discuss their results with the entire class. The teacher facilitates the activity by eliciting student input and guiding the development of understanding through student questioning.

The alteration of small group work and large group discussion accommodates the short attention spans evident in middle schoolers, holds students accountable, and increases learning.

OBJECTIVES

- Students will observe and describe various types of fruit.

- Students will classify the fruits as "dry" and "fleshy."

- Students will predict and determine the means of seed dispersal.

- Students will demonstrate the geographical distribution of the observed fruits.

- Students will research and summarize the nutritional and commercial value of fruits and seeds.

- Students will describe and appraise genetically engineered fruits.

- Students will explain the interdependence of plants and animals.

MATERIALS

- nut cups
- raisins
- dehydrator(s)
- a variety of fleshy and dry fruits
- containers to hold the fruits
- copies of "Procedures for the Student" page that follows this exercise.

TEACHING TIPS

- Provide a variety of fruits, such as:

— acorns
— pumpkin
— peanut
— grape or tomato
— oranges
— apple or pear
— maple seeds
— locust pods, tamarind, carob, or mesquite
— corn, oats, or wheat
— pineapple
— strawberry
— peach, cherry, plum, or coconut

— peas or beans
— cucumber, banana, kiwi, or citrus fruits
— dandelion or sunflower
— raspberry or blackberry
— iris or lily

• Acorns, maple seeds, wheat, locust pods, and so forth, can be saved from year to year by keeping them in a refrigerator.

• Have students bring dehydrators from home or increase their involvement by asking class members to construct their own dehydrators. There are several easy dehydrator construction techniques students can try.

• Check with the produce manager of a grocery store to see if it is possible to get donations of blemished fruit at reduced or no cost. The cost can be minimized by using only one specimen of each fruit type and having students rotate stations. Community connections can also be established by visiting a local seed company or greenhouse.

• This activity lends itself to many multidisciplinary connections. The English teacher can introduce American folklore with the story of Johnny Appleseed. Students can then create folklore of their own.

The social studies teacher can connect history and settlement of the United States with native plants, plants brought to the U.S. by explorers, Sterling Morgan and the establishment of Arbor Day, and the great effort that went into planting, harvesting, and using crops.

The math teacher can use ratios to relate seed size, plant size, and fruit size. Is the number of seeds proportional to the size of the plant? Can you tell from seed size if it is an annual or a perennial? The symmetry of fruits can also be explored.

The art teacher can have the students design seed packets. What types of information are on the packet?

Where these seeds are grown connects to geography. This activity provides a great time to study the transformation of humans from hunters and gatherers to farmers. The agricultural revolution, the resulting social change, and the impact on government are also relevant topics to explore.

Finally, dehydrating the fruits can be connected to the home economics/family and consumer science human survival skills' class.

PROCEDURE

1. Introduce the activity by distributing nut cups filled with raisins. Working in pairs, have the students describe their raisins. Someone will probably say that they look dry. Ask students to name other dehydrated fruits that they are familiar with. Why are fruits dehydrated? Is the nutritional value the same in fresh and dried fruits? Tell students that this is one of the questions they are going to investigate.

2. Begin the dehydrating process by having the students assist you in dehydrating some apples and oranges using a dehydrating machine. Ask the students to help develop a procedure that includes measuring and slicing the fruits and weighing them. The class will record data daily.

3. While the dehydration process is continuing, divide the students into groups of three or four and have them examine and record observations of 8-12 assorted teacher-provided fruit samples.

4. After 10-15 minutes, tell the students that fruits are classified as "dry" and "fleshy." Discuss what they think that means. Ask students to group their fruit samples accordingly.

3. Discuss student findings and generate definitions of dry and fleshy. Introduce the idea of

subdividing the fruits into smaller groups. Ask students to generate criteria.

4. Open the fruits. Look for seeds. Note any patterns, such as the number of sections in an orange. Discuss the findings with the whole class.

5. Divide the students into five expert groups of five students each. Each group will be responsible for learning about a specific topic and sharing the information with others. One group will research the nutritional value of the fruits. Another group will learn about genetically engineered varieties of the fruits. A third group will examine the various seeds and predict means of dispersal, and a fourth group will learn which seeds are sold or used in commercial products. The fifth group will categorize the fruits on the basis of where they are grown (look at geographical distribution).

6. Provide time for the students to research their topics.

7. Rearrange the groups so that a member of each expert group is now a member of a new group. Each expert presents the information he/she learned with the new group.

8. When the fruits are dehydrated, determine the percent of water loss and eat the fruits. Discuss how fruits might be dehydrated commercially. What are some other means of preserving fruits?

9. Have students summarize the value of fruits and their role in the life cycle of plants.

EXTENSIONS

• A fun activity is to simulate seed dispersal by spreading birdseed over a designated area. Have students take off their shoes and walk sock-footed over the area. Remove the seeds attached to the socks. Observe. Try to name them. Predict the type of plant that will result from each seed. Is there a relationship between seed shape and germination time? Design an experiment to find out.

• Explore factors that affect seed germination and plant growth. Design and conduct experiments to investigate variables such as light, temperature, moisture, soil type, competition, etc. Measure and graph results. Use seeds that germinate rapidly, such as radish, mustard, tomato, and turnip. You can also determine germination percentages.

• This is a great opportunity to introduce hydroponics and/or tropisms (gravitropism, phototropism, etc.).

• Connect to technology by researching examples of genetically engineered fruits such as seedless tomatoes, grapes, etc. Discuss pros and cons. Discuss whether the students think genetically engineered plants/fruits should be labeled as such.

• As a long-term project, plant seeds of native and hybrid plants. Discuss the trade-offs involved in developing the "perfect fruit" and the use of insecticides and fungicides to prevent blemishes on a fruit. Also, look into the development of various plants for specific climates. Discuss world hunger and water use concerns.

• Explore where fruits come from by examining flowers. Discuss sexual reproduction in plants. Compare/contrast with human reproduction. Discuss how florists stimulate flowering in plants. If possible, visit a greenhouse.

• Relate to nutrition by investigating the relationship of good health and fruits. Research the history of scurvy and other diseases.

• Research the life cycle of a plant. Be sure to include the history of the plant, the interdependence of the plant with other plants and animals, and the role of fruits.

SUMMING UP

Fruits play a vital role in a healthy diet, providing essential vitamins and a sweet refreshing taste. Fruit seeds have specialized characteristics that aid in dispersal by wind, water, and animals. We can control fruit characteristics by selecting plants with desirable traits (like navel oranges). A study of fruits can help improve the students' diets and increase their understanding of the interdependence of plants and animals.

ORIGINAL SOURCE

Chappell, Mary R. (1993). Fruit lab. In L.R. Sanders (Ed.), *Favorite Labs from Outstanding Teachers — Volume II* (pp. 130-136). Reston, VA: National Association of Biology Teachers.

The Fruit Lab — Procedure for the Student

Complete the data chart below and answer the following questions:

Name of Fruit	Description	Dry	Fleshy

ANALYSIS AND CONCLUSION

1. Discuss the importance of fruits.

2. Which fruits studied are more likely to have their seeds dispersed by animals?

3. Relate the structure of seeds to their method of dispersal. Give some examples.

4. How can the knowledge of fruits by used to improve our quality of life?

Chapter 4
Evolutionary Investigations

Variation and Adaptation at the Zoo

Adapted from an original activity by William F. McComas

Most of us are not consciously aware of the many variations present in organisms of the same species. Sometimes the differences are easy to notice, but many times the differences are subtle and require careful observation. The individual with characteristics best suited for its environment survives and reproduces. This principle is called "survival of the fittest" or "natural selection."

OBJECTIVES

- Students will visit a zoo.

- Students will investigate variation within a species.

- Students will link physical characteristics of organisms with the environments they inhabit.

- Students will predict future characteristics needed for an organism to survive if the environment changes.

MATERIALS

- photocopies of each worksheet at the end of this activity

TEACHING TIPS

- The accompanying worksheets target major principles pertaining to *natural selection.* They have been designed to foster classroom discussion by providing exciting illustrations of the principles involved. The individual sections may be modified for specific student groups, or each part may be used independently of the others.

• One major consideration relative to the potential success of this activity is the size and diversity of the collection at the zoo being visited. It is very important that the zoo have a large variety of animals, preferably from different geographic areas, with at least three representatives of each animal to be investigated. This may become easier with the new emphasis at zoos toward having more examples of each species, but fewer total species.

• For the first activity, it would be possible to use farm animals or the resources of a large local pet store or animal shelter. This exercise may also be performed with plants found at an arboretum or large nursery to illustrate that change over time is a unifying concept in all of biology, not just animals.

• Teachers may find it useful to consult the book *After Man* by D. Dixon (1981), published in London by Harrow House Editions, Ltd. This fascinating book makes predictions of what future creatures may look like based upon the present evolutionary trends, coupled with projections of the pattern of continental drift.

• Before visiting the zoo, meet with zoo personnel and enlist their help in planning the class trip. Most of the larger zoos have an educational department that can provide valuable suggestions and insights. Also discuss student behavior and academic expectations. Behavior problems are usually minimal on such trips, especially if parents or grandparents volunteer to help.

PROCEDURE

Part I: Variation Within a Species

The first section is designed to illustrate the principle of variation within a species. Students are given the opportunity to study a particular type of organism and establish that even organisms of the same species will show some variation within that species. Generally, physical characteristics are considered by students to be the principal factors that enable some individuals to survive, but there are also differences in physiology, behavior, and reproductive success. Although these factors may not be as apparent to the casual observer, they play just as big a role in the process of natural selection as physical characteristics do.

1. Before visiting the zoo, ask students what they expect to see at the zoo. What questions do they have? What particular animals interest them? List all student comments on the board.

2. Divide the class into pairs of students who have similar interests. Each student pair should have a different animal species to study while visiting the zoo. These animals are studied as a group; therefore, several representatives of the animal should be available. A quick look at the individual animals may reveal nothing unique, but a more detailed examination of many individuals will reveal subtle differences among them.

Part II: Adaptations for the Environment

Next, the students will examine in detail the natural environment in which the animal lives. Each pair of students will try to determine what characteristics appear to allow its chosen animal to fit well into that environment.

Part III: Similarities

1. In Part III, students are asked to find another animal that shares a similar environment with the animal each student pair selected in Part I. In this case, the environment can be a large physical environment (desert, forest, grassland, etc.) or perhaps a smaller scale nutritional environment (seed eaters versus fruit eaters in the same general area).

2. This section is designed for students to explore the idea that sometimes organisms in a

common environment may have similar adaptations even though they are not related. For example, whales and fish both have finlike structures that move them within their watery environment, but this is not a suggestion that the two animals are closely related. Pressure from the environment has dictated that, in order to be a contender within a given environment, animals living there must share many common characteristics. Organisms coexisting in a given environment will often have a number of adaptations in common as a result of the processes of change working on both populations at the same time.

3. Some students may be lucky enough to have found two organisms that live in similar environments in different parts of the world. For example, both the gerbil and the kangaroo rat live in the same type of desert environments, but the gerbil is native to the dry, sandy areas of Africa and Asia, while the kangaroo rat is found only in the deserts of North America. These rodents resemble each other in a number of ways and have almost identical food requirements. (They are also familiar to many students.) If they lived in the same area of the world, they would be in direct competition. It would be an interesting project to concentate on the differences between these two rodents and see how each is fine tuned for its specific environment. Such a project would require some research, but from this information, it may be possible to predict which animal would survive if both lived together in either the southwest desert of North America or in Asia.

4. In another similar example, the student may choose the deer and the kangaroo. both have similar nutritional requirements and, upon close inspection, are seen to have almost identical construction of their skulls and teeth. The head of a kangaroo and the head of a deer are very much the same but not because of a close family relationship. Deer, of course, are mammals and carry their young inside their bodies until birth, while the marsupial kangaroos raise their young primarily in an external pouch. There are many other examples of mammals and their marsupial counterparts that students may discover through research.

5. Examples such as those mentioned above show why an introduced species may effectively outcompete the native occupant of an environment. The transplanted or introduced organism may find itself well suited for the new environment but lacking the population controls provided by its own natural enemies.

Part IV: Predicting Future Evolutionary Trends

1. Finally, the students are asked to imagine what changes might occur in a group of animals if its present environment slowly changed. This part of the exercise represents a simplistic view of a complex process but is useful in encouraging students to apply what they have learned. Furthermore, it may be possible, through their answers in this section, to discern more about the students' understanding of natural selection.

2. Students should keep in mind here that, even if a small group of individuals in a population possesses an advantageous characteristic, this characteristic may not be easily passed on to the next generation.

3. With these cautions in mind, it is possible to suppose that a desert environment may become a woodland over a long period of time. Students can logically predict that those desert toads that already have a slight green discoloration may be "selected" by the environment since they are more effectively hidden in the green of the forest. At the same time, those tan-colored animals are not able to hide as effectively and may be removed by predators.

Part V: Conclusion

After returning from the field trip to the zoo, have the students complete the worksheets and discuss observations. Introduce Darwin and the term *natural selection.* Tell students that Darwin used the term "natural selection" to describe the process by which organisms with the most successful adaptations to their environments are most likely to survive and reproduce. Ask students to discuss the evidence of natural selection they have observed during their visit to the zoo.

EXTENSIONS

• Zoos try to recreate the animals' natural habitats. This requires a tremendous amount of planning and money. Have students predict the cost of maintaining the animals they have been studying while visiting the zoo. How much does each pair's specific animal eat daily? What kind of special care and consideration does it require? What is the minimum amount of space needed by the animal?

• Ask students to design an enclosure for penguins for a zoo in their home town. Discuss possible problems that penguins might encounter in captivity. Describe the considerations that must be addressed in meeting the needs of penguins. Make a scale model of the enclosure. Compare and contrast various designs. What issues need to be considered when moving animals to environments they have not adapted to?

• Have students create mini-posters of the specific animals they studied at the zoo. Use the posters in a colorful bulletin board display.

• Have students explore some of the causes for extinction of animal species. What are the consequences when various species disappear? What are some of the human activities that have increased the rate of extinction? What animals are in danger of extinction in your area? What can individuals do? Is protecting endangered species defying the process of natural selection? Why?

• Ask students to identify native and non-native animal inhabitants of their specific area. Explore the effects of introducing animal species into an area where they are not originally found. List some reasons why animals might be introduced into an area where they are not usually found.

• Explore how the depletion of natural resources changes the diversity of species in a given environment. Develop a class presentation that addresses the history of the natural resources in a specified environment, the uses of the resources, and possible solutions for solving the depletion of the resources. Encourage students to use computers, laserdiscs, graphing calculators, and other media when preparing the presentation.

• A possible performance assessment would be to have the students design and create an imaginary animal that could live in a habitat of the students' choice. Decide the adaptations that are necessary. Use these adaptations to create a critter that could survive and reproduce in a specified habitat. Give the critter a name, describe its food sources, habitat, lifestyle, and the advantages provided to it by its adaptations.

SUMMING UP

In this activity, students are able to explore the process of natural selection. They observe variation in heritable characteristics, identify some of the characteristics that aid organisms in surviving and reproducing in specified environments, and predict adaptations needed to survive if the environment changes.

ORIGINAL SOURCE

McComas, William F. (1994). Illustrating variation and adaptation at the zoo. In W.F. McComas (Ed.), *Investigating Evolutionary Biology in the Laboratory* (pp. 45-40). Reston, VA: National Assocation of Biology Teachers.

Variation/Adaptation at the Zoo — Procedure for the Student

Evidence of Variation and Adaptation at the Zoo

PART I — VARIATION WITHIN A SPECIES

1. Choose an animal in the zoo that is represented by at least three different individual specimens. WRITE the common and scientific names of the animals on the lines below:

Animal A

common name ______________________________ scientific name __________________________

2. What is the specific location of the animal in the zoo?

3. Examine your animals in detail and LIST as many individual differences as possible for the species in question. Example: Hair (long, short, or medium); Light brown vs. Dark brown fur color, etc.

<u>Characteristic</u> <u>Variation Seen Within the Species</u>

a.

b.

c.

d.

e.

4. In the space below, DISCUSS the advantages of variation within a species.

PART II — ADAPTATION FOR THE ENVIRONMENT

In this section, you are to examine the natural environment in which the animal you have chosen lives. Try to see what general characteristics make the animal fit well into that setting and suggest what other characteristics, if present, would make the animal less well suited for that particular environment.

5. WRITE a short paragraph that discusses the natural environment in which the type of animal you have chosen lives. Be very specific. Note — you may need to do some additional research here!

6. SELECT and LIST those characteristics which you believe will help the animal fit into its environment. Biologists refer to "inherited characteristics" that better enable an organism to survive in its environment as "adaptations." For example: Long fur to help the animal stay warm in cold temperatures, body color, etc.

<u>Adaptation</u> <u>Why Does the Adaptation Help the Animal Fit into Its Environment?</u>

a.

b.

c.

d.

e.

7. LIST a few general adaptations that would make the animal poorly suited to its natural environment.

<u>Adaptation</u> <u>Why Would This Adaptation Be Harmful?</u>

a.

b.

c.

8. By their very nature, zoos contain animals that are not adapted to the area. Special attention must be given to creating conditions in which animals can survive. Describe the special efforts taken by zoos to compensate for your animal's adaptations to its natural environment. How has the local environment been adapted to meet the needs of the animal you selected in Part I?

PART III — SIMILARITIES

In this section, you are to find another animal that lives in the same type of environment as Animal A. Note — The two animals chosen may both live in the desert, but they do not necessarily have to live in the same desert.

9. CHOOSE a new animal that lives in the SAME type of environment as "Animal A." WRITE the common and scientific names of the animal on the lines below:

Animal B

common name ______________________________ scientific name ______________________________

10. What is the specific location of the animal in the zoo?

11. EXAMINE "Animal B" and LIST the characteristics that it has in common with the organism you chose at the beginning (Animal A).

Both animals have:

a.

b.

c.

d.

e.

12. Why do you think two animals that share a common environment have so many characteristics in common? How could this similarity have occurred?

13. What do you think might happen if the two animals you have identified lived in not only the same type of environment but also in the same area?

PART IV — FUTURE PREDICTIONS

Finally, go back to the animal you chose first (Animal A) and try to imagine what would happen to this animal if its environment slowly changed toward one quite different from that seen at present. For example, you might examine an animal in a desert environment and predict what would happen to it if the environment slowly became more like a woodland.

14. RESTATE the common name of "Animal A" and the type of environment in which it now lives.

15. Suppose that for some reason the animal's normal environment slowly changes. CHOOSE a new environment into which the old one will change. DESCRIBE this new environment. Specifically, what will be different about it?

16. Choose five (5) characteristics seen in the animal at present and discuss what adaptations will be needed as the environment changes in order for the species to survive. For example, if a woodland slowly becomes a desert, the green coloration of a toad may not be an advantage. The green toad will be eaten because it is more readily seen by its prey than the brown species. The brown species is able to hide more effectively (survive) and thus reproduce.

Present Characteristic	Future Characteristic	Reason
a.		
b.		
c.		
d.		
e.		

17. Do you think that the animal in question will be able to live in the new environment proposed for it? To help you answer the question, think about the normal variation within the species. Do any of the individuals that you have observed have any of the characteristics which would enable them to survive and reproduce as the environment changes?

Demonstrating Population Growth

Adapted from an original activity by Duane H. Keown

This activity will graphically demonstrate that species grow and that the number of organisms an ecosystem can support depends on the resources available, nonliving factors important for growth (such as light and water), and the potential for overpopulation. Because of the overpopulation potential in natural populations, most of the offspring do not survive to reproductive age, and there is a "struggle for survival."

OBJECTIVES

- Students will count and graph worm numbers.

- Students will read and analyze graph information.

- Students will discover factors that limit population growth.

- Students will explore limiting factors of human population growth.

MATERIALS

- 4 red wigglers (purchased from a bait dealer)
- quart containers (possibly cottage cheese cartons) filled with peat moss and rich soil
- box of Total® or Wheaties® used as worm food
- graph paper or access to computer

TEACHING TIPS

- The ability of an organism or species to reproduce and survive is illustrated concretely by culturing some fast-reproducing organisms in a closed environment. Commercial fishing worms called "red wigglers" purchased from a bait dealer work well for this purpose.

- Populations grow when organisms have suitable resources. Students should observe that the larger the population gets, the faster it grows. If nothing stops the population from growing, it continues to grow faster and faster. However, what actually happens in nature is that most populations go through a number of growth phases. The population peaks, and then the organisms begin to diminish in size and numbers until there is nothing left.

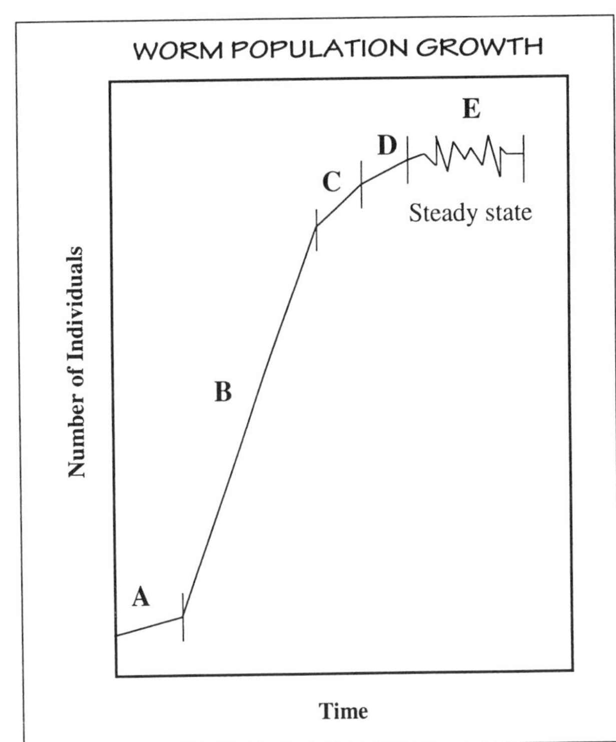

• The class graph of the worm population will probably look similar to the figure on the previous page. Whole group discussion is critical for students to think about the results and facilitate the sense making process. A possible class discussion may go something like the following:

— *Look at the graph on page 75. What is happening at A?* A is the initial growth. The worms begin to grow and multiply. This occurred slowly at first.

— *What do you think is happening at B?* The population begins to grow very rapidly. *Why does the population grow quickly?* Few animals are dying, and many are being produced.

— *Look at C and D. What is beginning to happen?* The population is growing at a slower rate. The population continues to grow slowly through D (the curve). *What does that mean?* Populations grow when more organisms are produced than are dying. Therefore, the birthrate exceeds the death rate. When birthrate equals the death rate, population growth stops (zero growth). This means that the number of red wigglers in the population remains the same, and no further major increases in the size of the worm population will occur.

— *What do you think E represents?* E is the so-called "steady state" when the average growth rate is zero. Although the population rises and falls slightly during this time, the rises and falls should average out.

— *Draw a horizontal line through the middle of the steady state region.* This line represents the "carrying capacity."

— *Once the red wigglers reached the carrying capacity of their environment, certain factors kept the population from growing further. What do you think some of those factors are?* Food availability, overcrowding, competition, etc., are some of the factors that affect population growth. *What do you think would happen if the population did grow larger?* Either the birthrate would decrease or the death rate would increase. *What do you think would happen if the size of the population grows smaller?* Either the death rate will decrease or the birthrate will increase.

— *How are natural populations kept from becoming extinct or overpopulated?* When a population is large and crowded, organisms are affected by competition, predation, parasitism, and crowding. *Discuss evidence that this is true.*

— Go back and graph the data regarding the population of your school and town. *What stage are they in? Why? What does that mean?*

• This activity is an ongoing project that requires an extended time period for completion. While the students collect data about the growth of their red wiggler populations, also explore some of the following related topics:
— predator/prey relationships
— parasitism
— mutualism
— competition
— role of camouflage
— renewable and nonrenewable resources
— human population growth
— various forms of pollution
— population effects on ecosystems.

• Some other possible projects include brainstorming environmental problems, deciding which of those problems interest students most, researching the chosen problems, and presenting the findings and possible solutions to the class. Project subjects may include:
— global ozone depletion
— global warming
— acid rain
— waste disposal
— resource depletion
— pollution
— extinction

Project Wild and Project Aquatic, available through state fish and wildlife agencies, is a wonderful source of activities to explore these topics.

PROCEDURE

1. Ask students to determine the population of their classroom. What is the population of the school building? What is the population of the city in which they live? Of the state? Since the students will probably not have the answers to these questions at their fingertips, ask them how they could find out.

Continue to explore the concept of population by discussing the following questions:

— Have these populations changed within the last 10 years? 20 years? 50 years? Ask the class to determine the actual numbers.

— What are some of the factors affecting the size of the population?

— How many individuals were born last year in the United States? How many died? What is the birthrate of the state where you live? What is the state's death rate?

— Why do we keep track of these numbers?

2. Tell students that almost any organism provided with ideal living conditions will experience a rapid growth in its population. In this activity, they are going to explore the population growth of red wigglers (earthworms).

Divide the class into groups of three or four students each. The members of each of these groups will work together to observe the earthworms, complete the graphs, and write a conclusion to the exercise.

3. Each group will place four worms (red wigglers) in a quart-sized cottage cheese carton filled with a media of peat moss and rich soil. A finely ground breakfast cereal provides a good diet for the worms. The cereal is sprinkled on top of the media, and the culture is kept moist and cool.

4. At two-week intervals, the number of worms in the cartons is counted, recorded, and graphed — time (horizontal axis) against numbers (vertical axis).

5. The students will also measure 10 worms at each counting and determine the average size since there is another serendipitous outcome for the students to see. Graph this information with time on the horizontal axis and size of the earthworms on the vertical axis.

6. Group members should complete the two graphs of the results of their earthworm observations and submit them along with a written report of their findings. Discuss group findings. Pool class data. How does group data vary from class data? (See "Teaching Tips" for possible class discussion questions.)

7. Relate the earthworm population exercise to human populations. Examine the history of human population growth. Compare population growth in several different countries. Describe the effects of increased human population on planet Earth.

8. Ask students how our way of life contributes to some of the environmental problems on Earth. Have them suggest ways we can change our lifestyle to lessen demands on the environment. Also discuss some of the environmental problems caused by rapid human population growth. Why has the human population increased so quickly? What may be the major limiting factors for the human population? Students should be prepared to explain their answers.

9. Discuss natural resource limitations, renewable and nonrenewable resources, and the effects

of war, disease, technology, severe weather (hurricanes, tornadoes, blizzards, drought), etc., on human populations.

SUMMING UP

This activity provides a great opportunity to actively involve students in a real example of population growth and to help them realize the implications of overcrowding (i.e., depletion of resources and accumulation of waste). The exercise also introduces students to the concepts of social responsibility and the need to be environmentally conscious.

ORIGINAL SOURCE

Keown, D.H. (1994). Demonstrating biotic potential. In W.F. McComas (Ed.), *Investigating Evolutionary Biology in the Laboratory* (p. 63). Reston, VA: National Association of Biology Teachers.

How Long Is a Long Time?

Adapted from an original activity by William F. McComas

It is easy to say that the first living cells appeared on Earth about 3.5 billion years ago, but few can really visualize the size of a number as large as 3.5 billion. To further complicate the issue, it is practically impossible to illustrate the expanse of geologic time to scale in a textbook diagram since a division even as small as a centimeter — used to represent one of the geologic periods — would result in a chart many meters long. For instance, on most textbook geologic timetables, it appears as if the Pleistocene Epoch and the Devonian Period lasted the same length of time because they take up the same amount of space. In reality, the Devonian was almost 25 times longer than the Pleistocene. In fact, this is the case even in the tables provided at the end of this activity. Such is the problem of scale when billions of years are reduced to a single page.

Also complicating the problem of scale is the fact that people usually view time from the perspective of their own lives. Something that happened 200 years ago may seem like ancient history, and yet geologic history covers millions and billions of years. This activity is designed to help students understand the vastness of geologic history.

An understanding of the vastness of size, time, and history can be accomplished by first exploring change that occurs in time periods that are familiar to the students, such as ice melting, the change of seasons, and erosion. The process is continued by having students investigate decades of time and discovering some of the evidence that tells us about the past. Finally, a connection is made to large spans of time, the eras and periods used to study the Earth's history.

A football field is used to create a scale model that helps students visualize large sections of time and provides a concrete example that enables them to think beyond their own experiences. The investigation of Earth's history is extended by encouraging students to pursue the answers to their own questions and then to present them to the class.

OBJECTIVES

• Students will gain a perspective of geologic time.

• Students will collect evidence and use it to tell about the past.

• Students will construct a scale model of geologic time.

• Students will infer interrelationships among biologic, geologic, and chemical events.

• Students will research the answers to their questions about Earth's history.

MATERIALS

- variety of slides or photos
- geologic timetable
- chart showing significant biologic events
- chart showing significant geologic events
- 65 or more 4x6-inch note cards

• several metric tape measures
• black, green, and red marking pens
• cards on wooden stakes on which students may draw or paste pictures of the various significant events.

TEACHING TIPS

• Preparing this unit of study facilitates the development of links in curriculum materials and activities that will connect the various disciplines. A team of teachers can effectively brainstorm questions, ideas, and materials that will strengthen interdisciplinary connections. Some initial ideas include:

— Discuss time lines and the relatively short span of American history compared to European history. Investigate if there are geometric cycles in history. Do wars, depressions, economic growth, etc., occur in predictable cycles? How does the answer to this question impact political decisions?

— Connect several aspects of science by exploring the mysteries of the Earth's crust, the fluctuating climate, and changing life forms.

— Imagining and writing about prehistoric times are fun ways to link science and language arts. Writing science fiction stories about prehistoric Earth uses what is known about the past to stimulate student creativity.

— The study of change over time can be connected to art by creating a mural depicting life on Earth during different eras.

— A review of proportion and its use in scale models is needed to develop the time line. The mathematics teacher can also study time, most reasonable units for measuring various time intervals, time zones, the 24-hour clock, and the use of timetables.

• To enhance students' learning, teachers should utilize all available resources, including community members. Interviewing adults about their lives (specifically about the past) is an excellent way to develop young people's ability to ask questions and to listen. This is also a great time to visit natural history and American history museums.

• The investigation of decades of time is included to help students think about how we know about the past. The inclusion of past and future decades helps the class realize the importance of using what we know about the past to predict the future.

• In this three-dimensional model, units of time are represented by units of distance. Markers placed at certain intervals corresponding to significant biologic and geologic events will make it possible to see what events preceded others and how much time or, in this case, distance passed between them. It is also possible for students to infer causal links between biologic and geologic events by visualizing them together.

• It is necessary to decide on the space in which the model of a geologic time scale will be set up. This activity is based on an actual football field that is 100 yards or 91.44 meters long. Calculate the scaling factor for your model by dividing the total length in meters by 4,600 million years. The calculation for a football field is **91.44 meters/4,600 million years = 0.01988 meters per million years.**

• It would be possible to adapt this idea to show the even longer period of time since the development of the universe itself, but the scale would have to be recalculated to allow all the events to fit into the football field. This may not be as effective, since the markers will now be much closer together. This approach is best reserved for a longer area.

• Two references that are strongly recommended to help to fill in the details for both students and teachers are *Life on Earth* by David Attenborough (1979) and *The Rise of Life* by John Reader (1986). These books are both well written and contain beautiful illustrations to tell the story of life's development in an engaging and intelligent way. The chronological treatment used makes both books quite useful for the purposes of extending this activity.

- For a visual representation of this approach you might want to show a videotape of the episode titled "One Voice in the Cosmic Fugue" from Carl Sagan's *Cosmos* television series.

PROCEDURE

1. Introduce the concept of time by showing students a variety of photographs or slides illustrating changes over various time intervals (seconds, minutes, hours, days, weeks, months, years). For example, a melting ice cube, a molted snake skin, autumn leaves, an eroding hillside or a river that has changed its course, photos of the Old West, dinosaurs, etc. Discuss differences in time required for the changes to occur.

2. Have students in pairs investigate changes that have occurred during a 10-year interval. Each pair will investigate a different decade. Start with 2010 and go backwards in 10-year intervals until all student pairs have a decade to explore. Look at the changes in dress, music, food, transportation, and news events (include earthquakes, volcanos, floods, politics, etc.). Present findings to the class. Encourage students to interview people who lived during the decade under investigation.

3. Discuss how we know about the past. What are the clues that help us know about past events?

4. Discuss how we know about the history of the Earth. Ask the students what clues help us unravel the mysteries of the past? Write down all suggestions.

5. Tell the class that evidence indicates that the Earth is 4.6 billion years old. This is an incomprehensible amount of time, but students can get a better idea of how much time that is by making a scale model of geologic time. The length of a football field will be used to represent the time that has passed since the formation of the Earth. Ask students how long a football field is (100 yards) and how many meters are in 100 yards. (100 yards x 3 feet = 300 feet. 300 feet x 12 inches per foot = 3600 inches. 3600 inches/ 39.37 inches per meter = 91.44 meters). So, in the metric system, the 100-yard-long football field measures 91.44 meters. One goal line is the *time zero goal line* that represents the present, and the other goal line (91.44 meters away) represents the far distant date that Earth began.

6. If 91.44 meters represents 4.6 billion years, then the distance needed to represent 1 million years on the model can be calculated (91.44 meters/4,600 million years = 0.01988 meters per million years). This number can be used to convert meters into the number of years that have passed for any time period or event.

7. With this important calculation in mind, student pairs are asked to determine how many meters are needed to represent the divisions of Earth's history. The history of the Earth is divided into eras, periods, and epochs.

For instance, according to the geologic timetable, the Devonian period occurred 48 million years ago, so 48 million years x 0.01988 meters per million years = 8.11 meters. A marker for this period should be placed 8.11 meters from the time zero goal line that represents the present. Using this method, the student pairs calculate the number of meters needed to represent each of the time divisions listed on the "Student Work Sheet/Geologic Timetable" that follows this activity.

8. Based on the previous calculations, students continue to complete the work sheets on "Geologic and Atmospheric Events" and "Biologic Events." For example, using the knowledge that multicelled plants and animals arose abut 700 million years ago ("Biologic Events" worksheet), it is possible to determine the location on the football field for that happening. *(700 million years x 0.01988 meters per milliion years = 13.92 meters.)* A marker for this event should be placed 13.92 meters from the time zero goal line that represents the present.

9. Marker cards will be made by the student pair from the 4x6 note cards listed in the "Materials" section. Assign each pair a time period and *four* events. Direct the students to use colored markers to label the 4x6 cards. (Label the geologic periods with a black marker, the significant biologic events with a green marker, and the geologic events with a red marker.) Fold the note cards as indicated in Figure 1 to form "tent shapes." They will then stand up by themselves on the ground.

10. Take the class members to an actual school football field. Have the students use measuring tapes to determine the distance from the goal line for each event or time period and place the 4x6 note card markers in appropriate places on the field.

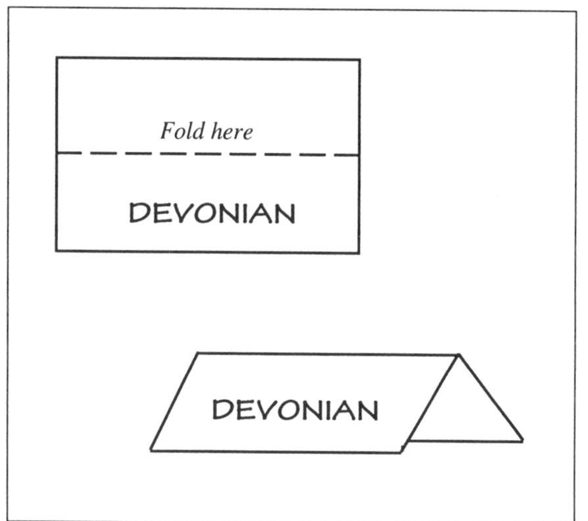

Figure 1. Folded card

11. Students will also draw signposts for the most interesting events. For instance, a picture of a fish may represent the Devonian period or a dinosaur may be used to indicate the Cretaceous period. Use the cards mounted on wooden stakes ("Materials" section) for this purpose and place each sign on the field at the appropriate location indicating when the event pictured took place.

12. Once the markers are all in place, it will be possible to actually "walk" through time from one end of the football field to the other and discuss the events and geologic periods in the order in which they occurred and in the proper scale.

13. Discuss the importance of the time scale and its uses. What connections can be made between geologic and atmospheric events and biologic events? If it has not already been discussed, introduce index fossils and their importance in distinguishing certain geologic time periods. Examine environmental changes and make predictions about future temperature fluctuations on Earth.

14. Brainstorm further questions that students may have. For instance, they may want to learn more about cave people, dinosaurs, the evolution of horses, etc. Have students investigate the answers to their questions and present them to the class.

EXTENSIONS

• Each student may create a timeline of his/her life or construct a concept map of geologic/ biologic time.

• Students may use a 12-month calendar or a 24-hour clock to represent the 4.6 billion years of Earth's history. For instance, on the calendar, January 1 indicates the beginning of Earth; April

30 is the earliest life; etc. (Each calendar day is almost 13 million years on Earth.)

- Obtain a geologic map of your local area and have students describe the sequence of geologic events suggested by the rock layers.

- Ask students to research actual remains of animals that have been found, such as wooly mammoths, or fossil life found in the Grand Canyon, etc.

SUMMING UP

The vast number of years that have passed since the origin of Earth have permitted a wide variety of events to occur that are of interest to virtually everyone. This exercise helps to connect the sciences and other disciplines together as students explore this enormous expanse of time.

ACKNOWLEDGMENT

The original activity from which this exercise was adapted was a national award winner in the Biology Laboratory Exchange Program sponsored by Prentice Hall Educational Book Division, Englewood Cliffs, NJ.

ORIGINAL SOURCE

McComas, W.F. (1994). How long is a long time? In W.F. McComas (Ed.), *Investigating Evolutionary Biology in the Laboratory* (pp. 31-39). Reston, VA: National Association of Biology Teachers.

Student Worksheet/Geologic Timetable

ERA	PERIOD	EPOCH	BEGINNING (Millions of years ago)	DURATION (Millions of years ago)	NUMBER OF METERS	MAJOR EVENTS
Cenozoic Era	Quaternary	Recent	Began 10,000 years ago			Civilization spreads. Human beings are the dominant form of life
		Pleistocene	2	2		"The Ice Age." Modern human beings present. Mammoths and other such animals become extinct.
	Tertiary	Pliocene	5	3		Fossil evidence of ancient human beings near the end of the epoch. Many birds, mammals, and sea life similar to modern types. Climate cools.
		Miocene	24	19		Many grazing animals. Flowering plants and trees similar to modern types.
		Oligocene	37	13		Fossil evidence of primitive apes. Elephants, camels, and horses develop. Climate generally mild.
		Eocene	58	21		Fossil evidence of a small horse. Grasslands and forests present. Many small mammals and larger mammals, such as primitive whales, rhinoceroses, and monkeys.
		Paleocene	67	9		Flowering plants and small mammals abundant. Many different climates exist.
Mesozoic Era	Cretaceous		144	77		First fossil evidence of flowering plants and trees. Many small mammals. Dinosaurs are extinct by the end of the period. Coal swamps develop.
	Jurassic		208	64		First fossil evidence of feathered birds and mammals. Many dinosaurs roam the Earth.
	Triassic		245	37		Beginning of the "Age of Dinosaurs." Insects plentiful. Cone-bearing plants present.
Paleozoic Era	Permian		256	41		First evidence of seed plants. Fish, amphibians and giant insects present.
	Carboniferous	Pennsylvanian Period	330	44		First evidence of reptiles. Many amphibians and giant insects present. Many large fern trees. Swamps cover many lowland areas.
		Mississippian Period	360	30		
	Devonian		408	48		"Age of Fish." First fossil evidence of amphibians and insects. Many different kinds of fish in the Earth's waters. The first forests grow in swamps.
	Silurian		438	30		First evidence of land plants. Algae, trilobites, and armored fish plentiful. Coral reefs form.
	Ordovician		505	67		Fossil evidence of jawless fish. Algae and trilobites plentiful. Great floods cover most of North America.
	Cambrian		540	35		"Age of Invertebrates." Fossil evidence of trilobites, clams, snails, and seaweed. Seas spread across North America.
	Precambrian	Proterozoic Era	4.6 billion	Almost 4 billion		Fossil evidence of bacteria and algae. Earth forms.
		Archeozoic Era				

Geologic Timetable — Answer Key

ERA	PERIOD	EPOCH	BEGINNING (Millions of years ago)	DURATION (Millions of years ago)	NUMBER OF METERS	MAJOR EVENTS
Cenozoic Era	Quaternary	Recent	Began 10,000 years ago		0.0002	Civilization spreads. Human beings are the dominant form of life
		Pleistocene	2	2	0.04	"The Ice Age." Modern human beings present. Mammoths and other such animals become extinct.
	Tertiary	Pliocene	5	3	0.10	Fossil evidence of ancient human beings near the end of the epoch. Many birds, mammals, and sea life similar to modern types. Climate cools.
		Miocene	24	19	0.4	Many grazing animals. Flowering plants and trees similar to modern types.
		Oligocene	37	13	0.72	Fossil evidence of primitive apes. Elephants, camels, and horses develop. Climate generally mild.
		Eocene	58	21	1.15	Fossil evidence of a small horse. Grasslands and forests present. Many small mammals and larger mammals, such as primitive whales, rhinoceroses, and monkeys.
		Paleocene	67	9	1.33	Flowering plants and small mammals abundant. Many different climates exist.
Mesozoic Era	Cretaceous		144	77	2.86	First fossil evidence of flowering plants and trees. Many small mammals. Dinosaurs are extinct by the end of the period. Coal swamps develop.
	Jurassic		208	64	4.14	First fossil evidence of feathered birds and mammals. Many dinosaurs roam the Earth.
	Triassic		245	37	4.87	Beginning of the "Age of Dinosaurs." Insects plentiful. Cone-bearing plants present.
Paleozoic Era	Permian		256	41	5.69	First evidence of seed plants. Fish, amphibians and giant insects present.
	Carboniferous	Pennsylvanian Period	330	44	6.56	First evidence of reptiles. Many amphibians and giant insects present. Many large fern trees. Swamps cover many lowland areas.
		Mississippian Period	360	30	7.16	
	Devonian		408	48	8.11	"Age of Fish." First fossil evidence of amphibians and insects. Many different kinds of fish in the Earth's waters. The first forests grow in swamps.
	Silurian		438	30	8.71	First evidence of land plants. Algae, trilobites, and armored fish plentiful. Coral reefs form.
	Ordovician		505	67	10.04	Fossil evidence of jawless fish. Algae and trilobites plentiful. Great floods cover most of North America.
	Cambrian		540	35	10.74	"Age of Invertebrates." Fossil evidence of trilobites, clams, snails, and seaweed. Seas spread across North America.
	Precambrian	Proterozoic Era	4.6 billion	Almost 4 billion	91.45	Fossil evidence of bacteria and algae. Earth forms.
		Archeozoic Era				

Student Work Sheet/Geologic and Atmospheric Events

Event	Millions of Years Ago	Number of Meters from Closest Goal
Worldwide Glaciations (average)	1.6	
Linking of North and South America with land bridge	5.7	
Formation of the Himalaya Mountains	15	
Collision of Indian and Asian Plates	35	
Separation of Australia and Antarctica	50	
Formation of the Alps	65	
Formation of the Rocky Mountains	70	
Opening of the Atlantic Ocean as the Eastern Hemisphere splits from the West	100	
Formation of Supercontinent – Pangea II	200	
Formation of coal deposits	340	
Oxygen reaches 20% (present level)	380	
Development of the Applachian Mountains	575	
Breakup of the Early Supercontinent	580	
Free oxygen reaches 2% in the atmosphere	600	
Formation of the Early Supercontinent	1250	
Free oxygen begins to build up	2500	
Period of no free oxygen	3700	
Oldest Earth rocks	3800	
Origin of the Earth as a solid mass	4600	

Geologic and Atmospheric Events — Answer Key

Event	Millions of Years Ago	Number of Meters from Closest Goal
Worldwide Glaciations (average)	1.6	0.032
Linking of North and South America with land bridge	5.7	0.113
Formation of the Himalaya Mountains	15	0.30
Collision of Indian and Asian Plates	35	0.70
Separation of Australia and Antarctica	50	0.99
Formation of the Alps	65	1.29
Formation of the Rocky Mountains	70	1.39
Opening of the Atlantic Ocean as the Eastern Hemisphere splits from the West	100	1.99
Formation of Supercontinent – Pangea II	200	3.98
Formation of coal deposits	340	6.76
Oxygen reaches 20% (present level)	380	7.55
Development of the Applachian Mountains	575	11.43
Breakup of the Early Supercontinent	580	11.53
Free oxygen reaches 2% in the atmosphere	600	11.93
Formation of the Early Supercontinent	1250	42.85
Free oxygen begins to build up	2500	49.70
Period of no free oxygen	3700	73.56
Oldest Earth rocks	3800	75.54
Origin of the Earth	4600	91.45

Student Work Sheet/Biologic Events

Event	Millions of Years Ago	Number of Meters from Closest Goal
Anatomically Modern Humans (*Homo sapiens*)	0.05	
Early *Homo sapiens* develop	0.3	
Development of *Homo erectus*	1.2	
Australopithecines and *Homo habilis* develop	3.2	
Development of Early Primates	35	
Extinction of the dinosaurs – "Great Extinction"	65	
Flowering Plants develop	140	
Dinosaurs are abundant	175	
First birds	180	
First mammals	220	
First dinosaurs	235	
Rapid expansion of living things – "Permian Explosion"	250	
First reptiles	300	
Development of the self–contained egg	340	
Trees appear	350	
First amphibians	360	
Insect–like creatures appear	400	
Earliest fishes	500	
Early shelled organisms	570	
Marine invertebrates abundant	600	
Multicelled plants and animals	700	
Advanced single cells	1000	
Development of eukaryotic cells	1400	
Early algae (blue–green) Gunflint formation	2200	
First life (single celled prokaryotes)	3500	

Biologic Events — Answer Key

Event	Millions of Years Ago	Number of Meters from Closest Goal
Anatomically Modern Humans (*Homo sapiens*)	0.05	0.001
Early *Homo sapiens* develop	0.3	0.006
Development of *Homo erectus*	1.2	0.01
Australopithecines and *Homo habilis* develop	3.2	0.06
Development of Early Primates	35	1.29
Extinction of the dinosaurs – "Great Extinction"	65	1.29
Flowering Plants develop	140	2.78
Dinosaurs are abundant	175	3.48
First birds	180	3.58
First mammals	220	4.37
First dinosaurs	235	4.67
Rapid expansion of living things – "Permian Explosion"	250	4.97
First reptiles	300	5.96
Development of the self–contained egg	340	6.76
Trees appear	350	6.96
First amphibians	360	7.16
Insect–like creatures appear	400	7.95
Earliest fishes	500	9.94
Early shelled organisms	570	11.34
Marine invertebrates abundant	600	11.93
Multicelled plants and animals	700	13.92
Advanced single cells	1000	19.88
Development of eukaryotic cells	1400	27.83
Early algae (blue–green) Gunflint formation	2200	43.74
First life (single celled prokaryotes)	3500	69.58

Chapter 5
Classification Studies

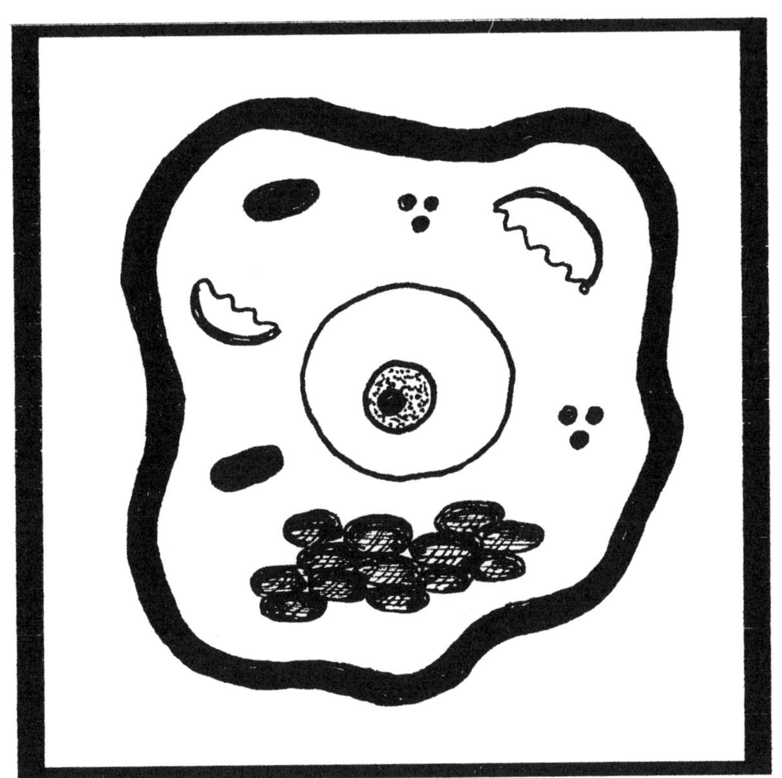

Teaching Classification with Music

Adapted from an original activity by Kathryn V. Lykins

Classification systems provide an organized approach to the study of the vast diversity of organisms that surround us. However, it is often difficult for teachers to engage students in the topic of biological classification. Students need to understand that "classification" is a means of grouping organisms by shared characteristics, that classification involves a hierarchical structuring of the living world, and that similarities and differences among organisms suggest how living things are related.

In discussing the nature and purpose of biological classification, textbooks typically introduce the topic by referring to the grouping of similar items in grocery stores or related books in libraries. Although all young people are interested in food and many are interested in books, these analogies lack interest and excitement. How can teachers present biological classification in a manner that will engage student interest?

An activity that has worked well is to introduce students to biological classification by having them classify music. A discussion of musical classification will have all students on task and will help them see the need for biological classification and even appreciate why phyla need to be further divided into classes, classes into orders, and so on.

OBJECTIVES

- Students will experience the need to organize/classify.

- Students will explore the nature of classification.

- Students will distinguish between arbitrary and fundamental bases of classification.

- Students will connect classification to their everyday lives.

MATERIALS

- blackboard or large sheet of poster board or newsprint that can be tacked up at the front of the classroom
- chalk or markers for writing on the blackboard or poster board
- student notebooks or notepaper for copying the finished classification groups developed by the class members

TEACHING TIPS

- The interdisciplinary nature of science in the middle school can be reinforced by involving teachers in other disciplines to further develop this activity. For example, the music teacher can discuss the attributes of various types of music and/or explore the evolution of music.

- This activity will also easily extend to a study of various cultures and geography. Students can select a region of the world and learn about the plants and animals that are found there and how they are like or unlike those found in other parts of the world.

PROCEDURE

1. Ask students to identify the name of their favorite singers or musical groups. As the students respond, write down the responses. Warning: Teachers should be prepared to use their best classroom management skills. Students who have previously displayed little or no interest in class will be calling out answers. Manage the activity so that everyone has a chance to participate. The number and variety of responses will indicate a need to organize or group the students' favorite music in some way.

2. The goal is to facilitate the organization of the music into three groups (a rap column, a rock column, and a country column). The teacher does not have to be particularly knowledgeable about popular music because the students will be happy to indicate what goes where. Accept their answers about grouping and mention that this is the way biological classification will be introduced to the class. Let the students continue suggesting names until the chalkboard is filled.

3. Subgroupings will probably come up as a natural part of the activity, but if they don't, the teacher can introduce them. Often someone will mention a "quiet storm" artist, such as Whitney Houston. ("Quiet storm" refers to romantic ballads that might generally be considered to be a type of rhythm and blues.) When asked which of the three columns this name should be placed in, students will often indicate the "rap" column, arguing that rap and quiet storm belong together because they are both "black" music. Ask the students if Motown, soul, rap, and quiet storm should all be grouped together as black music. Point out to the students that perfectly legitimate arguments can be made for that approach and equally legitimate arguments made for using the subgroupings of rap, Motown, quiet storm, and soul since these are four distinct types of music, although all were originated by black artists. The discussion of musical subgrouping is an excellent way to help students understand that there are differences of opinion among biologists about classification systems. Students can readily appreciate the comparison between differences of opinion regarding musical classification and differences of opinion regarding biological classification. They can also see the necessity of choosing a classification system and using it consistently.

4. Discuss the different systems of kingdoms now in use in biology and concentrate on the need for subdividing the three major musical groupings you have listed. Generally the students will indicate where the appropriate subgroups fall — perhaps with the subgrouping of black music as described above, perhaps with an insistence on dividing the rock category. Typically, students will indicate that certain names (R.E.M. and Metallica, for instance) don't "belong together."

This presents the perfect opportunity to make an analogy between the original three major groups (country, rap, and rock) and the kingdoms used in biology. Explain that just as it can be helpful to subdivide the rock category into smaller groups (such as classic rock, alternative rock, heavy metal, punk rock, soft rock, etc.) biologists subdivide kingdoms into phyla.

5. Turning the discussion away from musical classification and towards biological classification, ask the students to picture an animal in their mind and say, "Most of you have probably thought of some type of furry animal — a mammal." The next question is, "What other types of animals are there?" The ensuing discussion focuses on a general grouping of animals usually based on physical characteristics.

This is a great opportunity to introduce homologous structures and the difficulty in classifying animals solely on physical characteristics. Animals that look alike, such as dogs and coyotes, are only distantly related, while others may not look that much alike but are closely related (i.e., various breeds of dogs). A much more effective means of classification involves many different kinds of evidence, including DNA analysis.

After the students have discussed vertebrates and invertebrates, discuss the great diversity of animals found within these groups and the need to subdivide both vertebrate and invertebrate phyla into classes. The teacher will want to keep this simple, of course. Discuss mammals, birds, reptiles, amphibians, and fishes, but do not get into more technical classifications in this lesson. In discussing invertebrates, emphasize insects and mention that there are many different types of insects, so that class is divided into many orders.

6. Discuss problems associated with using arbitrary attributes of size, color, etc., to classify animals. Ask the students what they think is a more useful way to classify animals. Write the student ideas on the board. Focus the discussion on using increase in complexity to classify animals.

7. Using the "musical" method also provides teachers with the opportunity to emphasize the usefulness of classification. Ask the students to imagine two record stores, each as big as the biggest mall they have ever seen. Tell them that in the Big Unclassified Mall, all CDs, tapes and records would be arranged alphabetically. The "B" section would have the B-52s, the Beastie Boys, Garth Brooks, the Beatles, J.S. Bach (and all his sons), George Benson, the Black Crowes, etc.

The Great Classified Mall would have CDs, tapes and records arranged alphabetically too, but they would first be divided into sections as, in fact, they are in most music stores. Customers at the Great Classified Mall would find country, rap, rock, blues, bluegrass, rhythm and blues, gospel, contemporary Christian, jazz, and classical sections. Students will generally agree that they would prefer to shop at the Great Classified Mall.

8. Ask students to think of other examples of how classification is used in their everyday lives.

EXTENSIONS

• Ask students to consider similarities and differences among a wide variety of life that they see in their own environments.

• Have students explore how the depletion of natural resources changes the diversity of life in a given environment.

SUMMING UP

Through observing organisms, patterns of similarities and differences become apparent, and the degree of relatedness can be inferred. As more information becomes available, it is often necessary to change the classification system. Whatever system is used, classification enables students to see and understand more clearly the great diversity of organisms.

An added benefit to this exercise is that teachers and students learn a little bit about each other's lives and interests outside the classroom. Although it is usually fairly easy to guess which type of music a particular student will prefer, there have been some startling surprises. And always there are students who ask why jazz and/ or classical music is being left out. Moreover, in discussing music, teachers have a chance to validate all their students' musical tastes and point out that the world would be a very dull place if we all liked the same things.

Teachers can encourage students to be open to new experiences and remind them that people change and, because of this, it is necessary to be open to rethinking opinions and ideas from time to time. Often decisions about music, food, and academics are made at an early age, and people become trapped in those early patterns of "not liking" classical music, broccoli, or science.

Most teachers have no doubt often heard students say, " I don't like science," and they know that a large part of teaching science successfully is to get the students to like science at least a little better. To do that, it is necessary to capture the students' attention, and generally speaking, teachers have to get the students to see them as people to whom they can relate. These objectives, along with the objectives directly related to biological classification, can be achieved through this investigation.

ORIGINAL SOURCE

Lykins, Kathryn V. (1993). The musical method of teaching classification. *The American Biology Teacher, 55*(3), 182-183.

The Nuts and Bolts of Classification

Adapted from an original activity by Douglas J. Glasenapp

This exercise is an inexpensive and effective way to provide students with hands-on experience in constructing, using, and realizing the value of dichotomous keys. The dichotomous key reinforces the use of similarities and differences to classify organisms.

The introductory activity and the "Nuts and Bolts" exercise are usually completed in two class periods of 45 minutes each. Together, these two activities provide excellent vehicles for group discussions on such diverse topics as families of organisms, types of animals, similarities in fruits and animals, and hunting and fishing rights.

Possibilities for an interdisciplinary project are also included here. This long-term project might continue through the school year and even become a multi-year study that students take responsibility for and pride in managing.

OBJECTIVES

- Students will design, construct, and use a dichotomous key.
- Students will apply their knowledge of dichotomous keys to a new situation.
- Students will create dichotomous keys for local trees.
- Students will determine the best plant(s) for a specific location.
- Students will design and implement a school improvement plan.

MATERIALS

- an assortment of footwear
- 15 sets of assorted hardware (nails, paper clips, etc.)

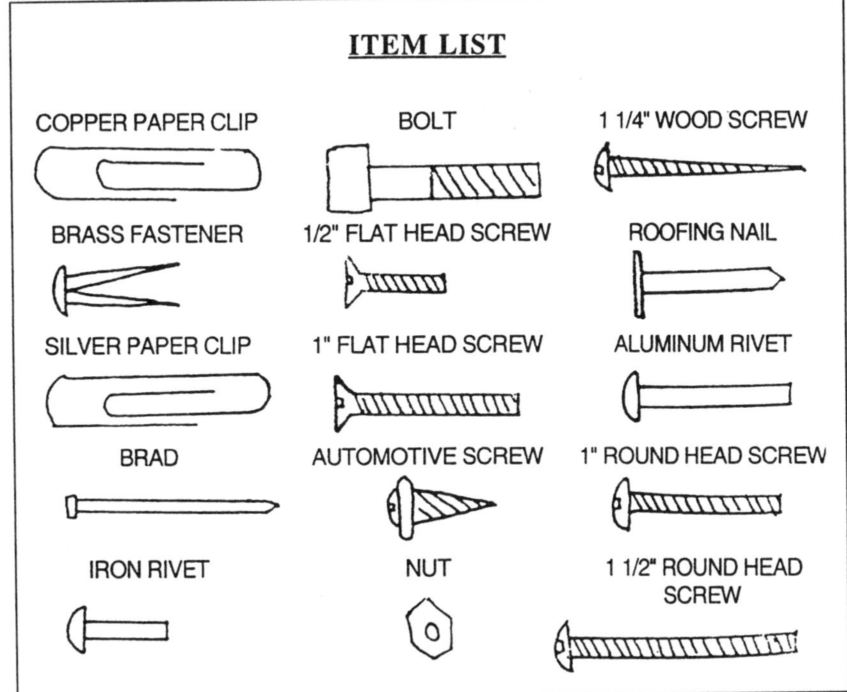

Figure 1. Items for "Nuts and Bolts" exercise.

- 15 small baby food jars or small containers
- rulers
- illustrative tree identification guides

TEACHING TIPS

• The materials used in this exercise are inexpensive, but it does take a little time to collect them. The best place to go is the school vocational technology department or a local hardware store. Please see Figure 1 on page 97 for suggested hardware items.

• Provide an assortment of footwear. Enlist the aid of fellow teachers to furnish a variety of shoes, boots, and slippers. Students love old go-go boots, platform shoes, Beatle boots, and other examples of days gone by.

• Obtain or purchase 15 of each hardware item. Keep each set of items in a baby food jar or other small container.

• Teachers may choose items other than those suggested here, but certain structures such as head type, threads, size, color, and shape should be considered.

• An easy and effective way to keep equipment from being lost is to assign a lab monitor in each class. The students check a jar out at the start, making sure everything is there, and check it back in at the end. The student monitor counts the items in each jar to insure none is missing. If an item is missing, the student usually finds it right away. It does not take that much time and it works! Try it! Normal cleanup time is four to five minutes.

• Any number of items can be used — sewing items, nails, shells, make-believe creatures, colored shapes, books, writing utensils, pots and pans, or whatever the teacher feels comfortable using.

• It is important that binomial nomenclature be correctly modeled. Be sure that, as students create names for the footwear, each name is underlined and only the *first* name is capitalized.

• There are several illustrative books available that can be used to create dichotomous keys for neighborhood trees. Community colleges and universities are good sources for local field guides.

• Interdisciplinary connections can easily be made by using the information collected by the life science classes (identification of trees present and knowledge of the type of plants best grown in specific locations) to design and implement a schoolwide plan to improve the school grounds. This could involve creating a nature trail, planting a butterfly garden or a wildflower garden, etc.

A good way to begin an undertaking of this kind is by writing down the reasons for the project and the goals to be accomplished as a result. Record all the plans in a written report that explains the situation, the reasons and goals for the project, and a possible action plan for accomplishing the task. Have students present the report to the principal and the PTA to enlist their support.

Also invite other teachers, students, and people in the community to help. The social studies teacher can have students map the area. The math students can measure the area and help in calculating costs and developing an operating budget. Students can make a scale diagram or scale model of the finished space. Moreover, the art teacher can help with aesthetic considerations so that the project will not only be functional but also beautiful. If possible, plan a field trip to a local plant nursery and look for means to involve the whole community.

When the project is complete, the students will be quite proud of what they have accomplished. Their pride in a job well done makes the project well worth the effort. It is also a wonderful opportunity to build community support and involvement in the school and a great introduction to social responsibility.

PROCEDURE

1. Introduce the activity by placing a varied assortment of footwear in a prominent location. As students enter the room, encourage observation and speculation. After a few moments of student exploration, inform the students that the footwear must be divided into two groups. Ask for suggestions as to how that task can be accomplished.

Have students observe and discuss what they see. Compare and contrast the footwear. How are the various samples alike, and how are they different? As the students call out ideas, probe their suggestions by asking additional questions, such as "What do you mean by a high or low shoe?" and "Can you think of another way you can convey that idea?" Once the criteria have been established by the class, have students direct the placement of the footwear in Group A or Group B.

Focus on the Group A footwear and ask students how they might divide Group A into two groups. As the process continues, keep a record of student responses on the board. See Figure 2 for an example of a dichotomous key for the footwear. Each sample of individual footwear should be given a creative, two-part "name" that consists of a *noun* and an *adjective*. Example: Comfy flats.

After Group A has been keyed out, draw student attention to the board. Explain that they have just created a dichotomous key, that each time they have had two choices based on their observations of similarities and differences, and that they used those observations to make decisions and to follow the directions to the next step. Continue by creating a key for Group B.

Dichotomous Key for Footwear

1. A. Has laces ... go to 2
   B. No laces present ... go to 5

2. A. Sole is made of a rubbery material ... go to 3
   B. Sole is hard and leather-like ... go to 4

3. A. Footwear does not extend above ankle ... Walking shoe
   B. Footwear extends above ankle ... Athletic romper

4. A. Toe is rounded ... Comfy flats
   B. Toe is pointed ... Aching toes

5. A.
   B.

Figure 2. Construction of a dichotomous key.

Facilitate a whole-group discussion of the value of this process and ask students where they think it might best be used.

2. Assess student understanding by having pairs of students construct and use a dichotomous key. Each pair of students receives a container of nuts and bolts (or other assorted hardware). Students should first make a drawing of all the items in their container. This is helpful in familiarizing students with the items.

3. Be sure to tell students not to use the proper names of the item when constructing the key. Creative names that are reflective of the item should be developed.

4. The students should use characteristics that they can readily see. Be specific. Exact measurements are acceptable, and rulers should be available for this purpose.

5. After completing the dichotomous keys, have the pairs of students exchange keys to determine if the keys work. The student-to-student interaction and comparison are very effective in clarifying student understanding.

6. Following the hardware activity, have students create dichotomous keys to identify neighborhood trees, such as maple, oak, birch, etc. What observations are needed to identify the trees? Use a variety of illustrative field guides to verify tree names and create dichotomous keys.

7. As an extension of the tree key exercise, students may research what species of tree is best for various school or neighborhood locations. Soil testing, monitoring of sunlight, rainfall, and student traffic must be considered. Working in small groups of three or four, students collect data on a selected aspect and present their findings to the class. After the group presentations, discuss actions that can be taken to beautify the school or neighborhood.

8. As a whole-class project, design and implement a schoolwide plan to improve the school grounds or neighborhood.

EXTENSIONS

- Volunteer to help a local organization or agency restock a pond or lake. What observations are needed to identify the fish?

- Use a dichotomous key to select a Christmas tree.

- Have students collect leaves or insects and identify them using a dichotomous key.

SUMMING UP

By discussing similarities and differences each time a new group of plants or animals is introduced, students are able to develop a usable understanding of classification. Take advantage of every opportunity to incorporate dichotomous keys into the middle level curriculum. With ample experience, students will develop their observation and reasoning skills and be able to use and create dichotomous keys efficiently and effectively.

SUGGESTED ILLUSTRATIVE FIELD GUIDES

Brockman, C. F. (1986). *Trees of North America.* New York: Golden Press.

Coombes, A.J. (1992). *Eyewitness handbook on trees.* New York: Dorling Kindersley, Inc.

National Audubon Society field guide to North American trees. (1995). New York: Chanticleer Press, Inc.

Petrides, G.A. (1993). *Peterson first guide to trees.* New York: Houghton Mifflin Company.

Zim, H.S. & Martin, A.C. (1987). *Trees.* New York: Golden Press.

ORIGINAL SOURCE

Glasenapp, Douglas J. (1986). The nuts & bolts of classification. *The American Biology Teacher, 48*(6), 362-363.

Life Science Scavenger Hunt

Adapted from an original activity by Judith L. Allard

A scavenger hunt is an excellent and fun way to end the school year, review some of the principles of a life science course, and find out what students really know. To find some of the items on the list, students will have to know something about various species' habitats and life cycles, as well as the interactions between organisms and their environments. Some of the items are open-ended and require students to be creative and thoughtful.

The scavenger hunt also provides an excellent opportunity to extend learning beyond the typical classroom, to generate student awareness of the world around them, and to facilitate the transfer of knowledge outside the classroom. It allows the teacher to assess his or her students' understanding of basic life science principles and their ability to reason and utilize knowledge. This activity encourages students to think critically to decide what evidence should be used and to form a logical explanation for choosing a specific item.

OBJECTIVES

- Students will practice reasoning, apply many of the biological principles learned throughout the school year, and communicate their understandings.
- Student groups will use the items collected, reference materials, and biological knowledge to create a written and pictorial record of their search.
- Students will practice *zero impact procedures* so that habitats and environments will not be disturbed or damaged.

MATERIALS

- paper lunch bags
- sealable plastic bags
- nets
- gloves
- plant, animal, and fungi identification guides
- list of student-generated safety precautions
- copies of *Procedures for the Student* pages (following this activity)
- list of items to be found (see Table 1 following this activity)
- student *Item Identification Sheet* (following this activity)

TEACHING TIPS

- Provide bags, nets, etc., for collecting the items on the scavenger hunt list — as well as the various references needed for identification.

- Define the boundaries of the scavenger hunt and discuss possible dangers in the specified search area, such as poisonous plants or animals, broken glass and other trash, traffic hazards, and other dangers.

- Remind students how to behave outside of the classroom. Caution students to be quiet around school buildings so as not to disturb other classes.

- Decide what you want the students to collect.

The list in Table 1 at the end of this activity is a suggestion, but teachers may adapt the list to reflect materials and species available in their own areas, if necessary.

• Vertebrate species were purposely omitted to simplify capture and release problems.

• The last item — "unusual item; one not found by another team" — was added after several classes had completed this exercise and found an unusual item, such as a molted snakeskin, that was not on the list.

• The time allowed for the activity is weather dependent. Allow for extra time out-of-doors, as this activity usually takes more time than might be expected. Additional time will be needed to complete the "item identification" pages and prepare for class presentations.

• You may want to extend the time period (for example, over a weekend) so that students can create a portfolio of their findings and/or use a computer to summarize and display the evidence they have collected.

• The points listed in Table 1 were determined by the relative ease or difficulty of finding the item or by the information needed by the team to know what they were looking for. None of the words on the list was defined for the students during this exercise, but all the words and terms had been used in class during the previous months of the course.

• Tell the students how the activity will be assessed. Points are given for describing the habitat of the item, providing other information about the species' life cycle, and explaining the precautions taken to protect the environment while collecting the data. Extra points may be given for providing the scientific name of the organism. Including as much extra information as possible about the organism may also boost student scores.

• Each group will make an oral presentation of the items found. Students will be expected to organize the evidence and explain the reasoning behind their choices.

PROCEDURE

Before the Lab

1. Collect the materials necessary for the activity.

2. Prepare an appropriate list of items to be found (see Table 1). The previous "Teaching Tips" section contains suggestions about point determination and extra credit possibilities for each item found.

3. Before the activity begins, check the area to be searched for safety hazards (cut glass, poison ivy, etc.). Help students generate a list of safety precautions to follow during the exercise. Be sure to have gloves or tools on hand for items that need to be handled indirectly.

4. Warn students to dress appropriately for the activity (long sleeves, sturdy shoes, etc.).

Day of the Lab

1. Be sure students know what is expected of them. Warn students that some items should be handled indirectly (with tools or gloves) and not with their bare hands.

2. Divide the class into teams of three or four students each and pass out *Procedure for the Student* sheets, copies of Table 1, and copies of the *Item Identification Sheet* to each group. Go over the sheets with the students to insure that they understand what they are looking for. Each team should also be given plant, animal, and fungi identification guides to help with identifying each item found.

3. Let the student groups know how much time

they will have to search for the items on the list. Student groups should be given extra time (possibly one class period) following the end of the search activity to complete their item identification pages and prepare a short presentation of their findings for the class.

4. In addition to locating as many of the items on the list as possible, each student team will create a map of the search area. The map will consist of a drawing of the area and sketches of the "findings" in the places they were found. A legend indicating the map scale and explaining any symbols used by the team will also be included on the drawing.

5. After student groups have found each specified item, members will need to explain where they found the item, why they think it was there, how the item fits the description in Table 1, and what they think will happen if this specific item is not involved in the ecosystem.

EXTENSIONS

This activity can be extended into a pre-course and post-course format whereby student groups can be asked to go out into the designated search area at the start of the year's course and bring back items from nature that they find interesting. All items found can be brought back to the classroom, placed in a pile, and then separated according to their similar characteristics. The concepts of classification and the "five kingdoms" can be introduced at this point, as students determine which items fit into the Plant Kingdom, the Animal Kingdom, etc.

Of course, in this way, the initial species studied will be limited to organisms available in the search area and the things of most interest to the students. However, throughout the school year, other organisms studied can be added to the classifications, and a final list can be compiled for the search at the end of the year, as previously described. Therefore, the list is directly related to the students' own environment and the species studied throughout the course.

Students can transfer the information from their team to a class map. The information each team contributes will form an overall perspective of the area.

SUMMING UP

This exercise provides students with an excellent chance at the end of the year to use some of their accumulated knowledge and apply it directly to their own environment. The activity can be refined from year to year to reflect changes in the course, the environment, or the level of the students.

ORIGINAL SOURCE

Allard, Judith L. (1991). Biology scavenger hunt. In D.S. Sheldon & J.E. Penick (Eds.), *Favorite Labs from Outstanding Teachers* (pp. 24-26). Reston, VA: National Association of Biology Teachers.

Life Science Scavenger Hunt — Procedure for the Student

This activity will take you out-of-doors on a scavenger hunt to search for items and organisms that we have studied throughout the year. Drawing on the knowledge you have gained from your studies in this course and the reference materials provided, you and the members of your team will find the items on the list in Table 1 and use them to complete the information requested on the "item identification" sheets.

For each item found, you will be asked to name the organism, provide a brief description of the area (habitat) where you found it and any other important information that you know about it, place it on your area map, and attach the item to the sheet or draw a sketch of it on the page. Items that are too large to be attached to the page should be labeled clearly and placed in a box to be submitted with the item identification sheets at the end of the exercise.

Following the hunt, you and the members of your group will prepare a brief presentation about your findings to the class. Your grade for this exercise will be based on the number of points earned for each correct item found on the search list, a completed map, detailed habitat descriptions, and extra information provided about the items found by your team.

Good luck and good hunting!

PROCEDURE

1. Collect as many of the items on the scavenger hunt list (Table 1) as possible. All materials should be collected with as little disturbance to the environment as possible. Live animal specimens should be collected only if they can be returned safely and without damage to them or you.

2. Fill out an *Item Identification Sheet* for each item you find. Be sure to provide as much of the requested information as possible (habitat description, information about the species' life cycle, and precautions taken to protect the environment while collecting the data). Attach the item to the sheet or draw a sketch of the organism on the page. If the item is too large to attach, label it clearly and place it in a box to be submitted to the teacher along with the item identification sheets at the end of the exercise.

3. Create a map or sketch of the area. Draw the area and include sketches of the organisms in the places where you found them. Be sure to include a map legend to explain the size of the area (map scale) and any symbols your team used on the drawing.

4. When you return from the hunt, you will be given time to complete your item identification sheets and prepare a brief class presentation of your findings. Your presentation should include the items found and the reasons for your choices.

5. Submit the items, map, and identification sheets to your teacher at the end of the activity. Your team must correctly identify each item you submit in order to earn points. For example, if you submit an oak leaf for a maple leaf, you will receive a score of zero for the oak leaf.

6. Extra points will be given for providing information about each species' habitat, life cycle, etc., so be sure to write down everything you know about each item.

Table 1. Scavenger Hunt List

Item Found (point value in parentheses)

1. A feather (1)
2. One seed dispersed by wind (1)
3. Two different seeds dispersed by animals (2)
4. Exactly 100 of something* (3)
5. A maple leaf (1)
6. An oak leaf (1)
7. A compound leaf (1)
8. A thorn (1)
9. One camouflaged insect (3)
10. Something with a geometric pattern* (1)
11. Part of an egg (not chicken) (3)
12. An example of an adaptation for our climate* (2)
13. A piece of fur* (3)
14. Evidence of human impact (1)
15. Evidence of succession (3)
16. Something beautiful* (2)
17. A leaf that has been chewed *(not by you)* (3)
18. Something that makes noise* (3)
19. Something that surprises you that you can find it in this location* (1)
20. Something soft* (2)
21. A sun trap* (3)
22. A bone *(double points if identified)* (4)
23. A owl pellet (10)
24. A fungus (3)
25. A second species of fungus (3)
26. Something that could be recycled (2)
27. Something spherical* (2)
28. A beetle (2)
29. A spider (2)
30. An insect larva (2)
31. A soon-to-be fossil (3)
32. Evidence of predation (3)
33. Evidence of animal presence* (2)
34. An example of a natural product that is used in its raw form* (3)
35. An example of interdependence (3)
36. Evidence of the effect of abiotic factors (soil, water, temperature, etc.) on plant growth (3)
37. An example of selective breeding (2)
38. Something you found that you would like to add to the list (1)
39. An unusual item — one not found by another team (5)

(These items must not be made by humans. They must be from the natural world.)*

Life Science Scavenger Hunt — Item Identification Sheet

Team Members ____

Common Name of Item ____________________________________

Scientific Name of Item *(optional)* ____________________________

Description of area (habitat) where the item was found.

Describe how the item fits the description in Table 1.

What do you think would happen if this specific item were not involved in the ecosystem?

What precautions did you take to protect the environment while collecting your data?

Additional information *(use the back of this sheet if necessary).*

Attach item to this sheet or draw a sketch of it below.

About the Editor

Catherine A. Wilcoxson is an Associate Professor of Biology Education at Northern Arizona University in Flagstaff, Arizona. She holds a B.S. in biology from Midland Lutheran College, Fremont, Nebraska; an M.S. in educational administration and supervision from the University of Nebraska in Omaha; and a Ph.D. in curriculum and instruction from the University of Nebraska at Lincoln.

Wilcoxson currently serves as NABT's Secretary/Treasurer and is the former chair of the NABT Publications Committee. In 1994, she was presented the Award for Excellence in Encouraging Equity by NABT's Role and Status of Women in Biology Education Section.

A former middle and secondary level science instructor, Dr. Wilcoxson's duties at Northern Arizona University include supervising student teachers and teaching science method classes and laboratory techniques classes for prospective middle and secondary educators. A caring and committed professional, she has been and is now actively involved in many efforts to enhance science education, including:

- Conducts workshops for K-12 teachers to aid implementation of the National Science Education Standards.
- Serves as Editor of Guidelines for Teacher Preparation: Mathematics and Science.
- Serves as a reviewer for the Journal of College Science Teaching and The American Biology Teacher.
- Serves as an expert panel member for the Council of Chief State School Officers to review state science framework documents (1994-1996).
- Writes for a distance learning class for the University of Nebraska, Lincoln (Communication, Learning, and Assessment in a Student-Centered System Project).
- Recently coordinated Nebraska's Mathematics/Science Framework Project (a three-year federally funded project to enhance math and science education in Nebraska) and served as editor of the framework document and guidelines.